GW00640665

VALUES OF

Agrarian
Landscapes

ACROSS EUROPE AND
NORTH AMERICA

VALUES OF AGRARIAN LANDSCAPES ACROSS EUROPE AND NORTH AMERICA

AUTHORS:

Paul Terwan, Mark Ritchie, Wouter van der Weijden, Gerwin Verschuur, Jan Joannides

ART DIRECTION AND DESIGN:

Brett Olson

A PROJECT OF THE:

Centre for Agriculture and Environment

Renewing the Countryside

Institute for Agriculture and Trade Policy

VALUES OF AGRARIAN LANDSCAPES ACROSS EUROPE AND NORTH AMERICA

Authors   Paul Terwan, Mark Ritchie, Wouter van der Weijden, Gerwin Verschuur, Jan Joannides

Art Direction   Brett Olson

Contributors

Europe:

Hervé Cortot
Paraskevi Dilana
Piotr Marczakiewicz
Juan J. Oñate
Patrizia Rossi
Thordis Samuelsson
Willem Vos

North America:

Andi McDaniel
Monica Siems
Michelle Wilwerding

Project Partners

Centre for Agriculture and Environment
Renewing the Countryside
Institute for Agriculture and Trade Policy

Publisher

Reed Business Information
P.O. Box 4
7000 BA Doetinchem, The Netherlands
Projectmanager: Rients Koopmans
Tel.+31 314 349871 E-mail: agriboek@reedbusiness.nl
www.agriboek.nl

ISBN-90-5439-147-2

First Printing

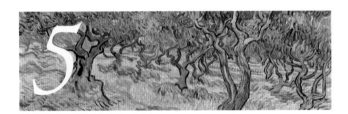

TABLE OF CONTENTS

PREFACE

We are blessed with a world of beautiful and varied landscapes — natural and wild, cultivated and agrarian. This is a book about one group of these, the working landscapes that include farming, grazing, horticulture, and related human activities. These landscapes not only produce food and fibre, they also provide renewable energy, ecological services, conservation of cultural heritage, social cohesion and biological diversity.

This book celebrates and explores these agrarian landscapes that are crucial to our physical and psychological well-being but rarely considered indepth. We have chosen to use examples in both Europe and North America to help provide a context for showing different kinds of agrarian landscapes. In each instance we explore the range of benefits and values to all of society and the challenges or threats that they face. At the same time, we look at the public policies and incentives being used to help foster more sustainable development in the regions where these landscapes exist, and we explore private initiatives by landowners, farmers, businesses, conservationists and communities to protect and preserve the benefits or to overcome the challenges.

Many of the benefits of these agrarian landscapes are common to both continents. Creation and protection of habitat for wildlife is important in many regions, along with providing priceless ecological services like the absorbtion of rainfall. Cultural heritage and social connections cannot be overlooked, especially in a time when the tearing of our social fabric seems dangerous.

As valuable as these benefits are to all people and the planet, there are powerful threats that cannot be ignored. Economic hardship for most of the people who work the land has created pressure to intensify or industrialize in ways that cancel out many of the benefits of these landscapes, especially ecological services and habitat, or has resulted in displaced families who have left the land because of inadequate income. Some international policies, especially in the financial and trade areas, have tended to work against the people on the land who are responsible for maintaining and passing on these valuable human and ecological assets.

Recognizing both the amazing benefits and the challenges, policy makers at the local, province, and national levels have developed and are implementing many innovative programs to protect and to provide incentives for the preservation of these valuable working landscapes. While Europe and North America have different approaches in many instances, the similarities standout and are increasing. In addition, the private initiatives, like regional labelling and special marketing approaches, are surprisingly similar on both sides of the Atlantic.

We come away from creating this book very hopeful. We are even more certain of the values that agrarian landscapes create and bring to all of our lives, even when we know full well the difficulties. What makes us most hopeful is the recognition of the benefits and threats and how this is reflected in renewed commitments on the part of society as a whole, through our governments and policymakers, and by the incredible creativity and tenacity of the people on the land fighting to preserve and protect this treasure we have been entrusted with for this generation.

In this time of great world tension and unusually strong feelings in the context of US and European relations, this book and the process by which it was made is an important reminder of that which binds us at a physical and cultural level. This book

can make a contribution to remembering that we are all on this blue-green planet as a result of grace and that we can share that gift with future generations if we act thoughtfully and responsibly.

We want to express our deep appreciation to those who encouraged us and supported us in this project, especially Cees Veerman, the Dutch minister of Agriculture, Nature, and Food Quality. One of his predecessors, Jozias van Aartsen, in 1997 supported the first Renewing the Countryside book that has helped inspire this process. With this appreciation, we also remind the readers that only the authors are responsible for the text and we welcome your comments and ideas.

Wouter van der Weijden
Director, Centre for Agriculture and Environment
Culemborg, The Netherlands
www.clm.nl

Mark Ritchie
Board Chair, Renewing the Countryside
President, Institute for Agriculture and Trade Policy
Minneapolis, USA
www.renewingthecountryside.org; www.iatp.org

INTRODUCTION

Agriculture is not just farming. In addition to producing food and fibre, many forms of agriculture also create a wide range of social, cultural, scenic and natural values and benefits.

Europe and North America both have an overwhelming variety of beautiful agrarian landscapes: from lowland grain fields to mountain pastures, from moist grasslands to semi-arid grain steppes, from cold grazed tundras to hot Mediterranean vineyards, and from nearly treeless corn belts to luscious orchards. Some of these landscapes are shared by Europe and North America. Others are unique. For instance, North America has no cork tree orchards and also lacks large areas of coastal lands below sea level, as found in the Netherlands. Extensive prairies with free roaming wildlife are still found in North America, but they have almost disappeared in Europe.

Apart from offering scenic beauty, many agrarian landscapes also offer natural benefits. They are home to a wide variety of plant and animal species, including species rarely found in other habitats. Without agriculture such spectacular birds as the Great Bustard in Spain would come close to extinction. Many of these landscapes also represent cultural and heritage values such as historical field and settlement patterns and unique regional products. Others are important in managing natural resources, such as absorbing and purifying rainfall and melting snow. Still others play a key role in preventing the urbanization of green spaces, or function as buffer zones surrounding nature reserves. Thus agriculture in many places, though not all, is a genuine multifunctional sector.

These agrarian landscapes depend on farming and grazing as central activities. Since they are 'working landscapes' their future is closely connected with the future of agriculture and with the people who work the land. Unfortunately, this mutual dependency presents a number of serious challenges. Many of these landscapes are losing some of their most valuable attributes and benefits. Sections of the most fertile land are being taken out of production due to urbanisation, often paved over in ways that make water absorption impossible. Farms in some regions are being abandoned due to a poor economy or increased climate instability, and the land is becoming neglected. Some of the land still utilized for agriculture is losing much of its ecological value through the hyper-industrialization of farming.

Most alarming is the fact that many of these developments may be irreversible. Once a field had been paved over for a road or parking lot, it will never become green again. Abandoned land is rarely reclaimed, at least not as long as farmgate prices remain low. Once large-scale factory farming becomes dominant, there is little chance the countryside will regain its lost scenic, cultural and biological values.

Some of these problems grow out of human failures — the disconnection between agricultural development and landscape management. Why is this happening? What are the driving forces? Some people blame landowners seeking excess profit from intensification and enlargement. Others emphasize the increasingly global market economy with its heavy competition and rules that consciously drive farm gate prices down. Still others point at the agri-industrial food corporations and supermarket chains. And finally, some people mention consumers who appear reluctant to pay the prices necessary to keep agriculture diverse and multifunctional.

There are grains of truth in each of these explanations. Some of the main driving forces include:

- **Increasing competition** via international markets as a result of growing economic unions and new global trading rules and agreements, resulting in downward pressures on prices that threaten farm family economic survival.
- **Power imbalances in the food chain**, where processors and supermarkets are driving farmers to produce in one-dimensional ways.
- **Technological developments** that reinforce the trend towards monocropping and narrow-focus efficiency.
- **Lack of adequate policies** to help maintain valuable landscapes and the underlying agricultural systems and practices.
- **Lack of effective and accessible markets** for the ecological goods and services and cultural values of agriculture.

Is it possible to preserve these valuable landscapes and their multiple benefits for future generations? That question we will leave for the last chapter. Let us first take a look at a variety of these landscapes and their values, functions and contributions. The following chapters present landscapes in both North America and Europe, outlining the values at stake and some of the people involved. We also highlight the challenges facing these landscapes, along with public and private actions that have the potential to help renew these countrysides.

LOWLANDS, WETLANDS & FLOODPLAINS

Whereas large parts of the world struggle with water shortages, there are some regions where it is the abundance of water that poses the greatest challenge. Water as a shaping element of the landscape and a dominant influence on land use can be found around the world in floodplains, lowlands, and wetlands. The sources of water that affect these landscapes include rainfall, groundwater, and the flooding of seas and rivers. In this chapter, we will take a closer look at several landscapes where water dominates.

Waterlogged landforms called peat bogs can be found throughout Europe. Most peat bog landscapes depend on rainfall, but a few are created by groundwater. In Europe, groundwater-fed bogs are found mainly in the Netherlands, the northern part of Germany, and some small areas near the coast of western France. These lowlands were originally peat marshes and swampy forests, but have been cultivated since the tenth century. One of the most outstanding examples of a peat bog landscape is found in the western Netherlands, where a 175,000-hectare 'Green Heart' of peat lowland has been preserved in one of the world's most densely inhabited regions.

In North America there is a large stretch of land in the Northern Great Plains where millions of tiny wetlands called 'prairie potholes' dot the countryside. Straddling the centre portion of the border between the United States and Canada, this special landscape provides a seasonal home for more than half of the continent's migratory waterfowl. The region serves as an excellent example of the complex interplay of farming, water, and nature.

Floodplain landscapes are common throughout Europe and North America — even tiny rivers and streams can flood adjacent farmland. However, many large-scale floodplains have been dramatically altered through increased drainage and engineered stabilization of watercourses. In the United States, almost all of the major rivers in agricultural regions are controlled in an attempt to prevent flooding and to facilitate transportation. Europe still has some large-scale, relatively unaltered floodplains, especially in Central and Eastern Europe. Some of the most significant include the valleys of the Morava River (where it forms the border between Austria and the Czech and Slovak Republics), Hungary's Tisza River, and the Biebrza River in Poland. The Biebrza River provides an especially good example of an intact system of natural, semi-natural and cultivated floodplain landscapes and habitats.

This chapter will explore the complex interplay of farming and nature that distinguishes these landscapes where water dominates.

The 'Green Heart' of the Netherlands

Many visitors to the western part of the Netherlands are surprised to learn that the area's low grasslands are below sea level. Since the tenth century, humans have shaped this landscape by draining and cultivating the groundwater-fed peat bogs and marshlands. The landscape, called the Green Heart of the Netherlands, has a history of continuous struggle against the water: centuries ago, dykes and mills were already being built to create and maintain conditions suitable for farming. But as the land is drained, the soil settles, so the land continues to sink further below sea level. As a result, efforts to pump out the water must be intensified every few decades.

For centuries, dairy farming has been the predominant agricultural activity in this region. In the past, pig farming was a significant secondary enterprise, with the by-products of cheese-making serving as feed for the pigs. Dairy farmers in the Green Heart have more or less adapted to the wet conditions and have found innovative answers to the challenges of their waterlogged landscape, such as the development of specialized machinery.

Das Torftiefland im sogenannten Grünen Herzen von Holland wird vorwiegend als Weideland für Milchvieh benutzt. Die sehr langen, aber schmal geschnittenen Landparzellen sowie die zahlreichen Wasserabzugsgräben schaffen eine einzigartige Landschaft. Die Artenvielfalt ist hier sehr reich: Hier können die seltene Uferschnepfe sowie Pflanzenarten wie die Sumpfdotterblume gefunden werden, die typisch für Feuchtbiotope und nasse Lebensräume sind.

Las bajas tierras turbosas del denominado "corazón verde" de Holanda se utilizan sobre todo para la ganadería lechera. Las larguísimas aunque estrechas parcelas y los numerosos diques conforman un paisaje único. Su biodiversidad es muy rica e incluye aves como la poco frecuente aguja colinegra y especies vegetales típicas de climas húmedos como la hierba centella.

Les basses terres tourbeuses du Cœur Vert de la Hollande sont principalement consacrées à l'élevage laitier. Les parcelles très longues et étroites ainsi que les nombreux fossés en font un paysage unique. La biodiversité est riche. On y compte un oiseau rare, la barge à queue noire, ainsi que des espèces végétales typiques des zones humides, telle que la populage des marais.

The peat lowlands in the Green Heart of Holland are predominantly used for dairy farming. The very long but narrow parcels and the numerous ditches create a unique landscape. Biodiversity is rich and includes the rare Black-tailed Godwit and plant species typical for moist and wet conditions such as the Marsh Marigold.

Values and Benefits

- **Landscape.** Cultivation of the marshes has resulted in a uniquely patterned landscape, especially as seen from above. Long, narrow grassland parcels are surrounded by ditches and cultivated in circular and rectangular patterns that meet at different angles. Some of these grasslands parcels are up to two kilometres long and only 30 to 40 meters wide. From the air, these grasslands seem to float on the water. Some literally do.
- **Biodiversity**. The Green Heart region's wet grasslands and marshy elements like reedlands harbour a great variety of specialized plant and bird species. For instance, the area's high water table and the openness of the landscape nurture large numbers of grassland birds like the Lapwing, the Redshank, and the internationally rare Black-tailed Godwit. Half of the European population of godwits breeds in the Netherlands.
- **Cultural heritage**. The area carries centuries of cultural history, including archaeological remains dating from the Iron Age to the Roman period, old fortifications and church roads, and other historical treasures.

Die Landschaft wird durch eine Abnahme der Landwirtschaft als Ergebnis von relativ hohen Produktionskosten in Kombination mit zurückgehenden Einnahmen aus der Milchwirtschaft bedroht.

El paisaje está amenazado por el declive de la agricultura, provocado por la combinación de los altos costes de producción y la caída de las ganancias de la ganadería lechera.

Le paysage est menacé par le déclin de l'agriculture, en raison de coûts de production assez élevés, liés à une chute des revenus tirés de la production laitière.

The landscape is threatened by a decline in agriculture, the result of relatively high production costs combined with falling dairy revenues.

Challenges and Threats

- **Urbanisation.** The Green Heart lies in the centre of one of the most densely populated areas in the world. As a result, more and more farmland is being sacrificed to commercial and residential development.
- **Decreasing profitability for agriculture.** While agriculture is the main economic activity on this landscape, producers face relatively high production costs (caused by the high water tables and limited accessibility of the land) together with decreasing dairy revenues (due to falling prices).
- **Farming practices.** Farming on this wet landscape requires drainage of the soil, which, in turn, causes the soil to settle and the peat to oxidize. Ultimately, the peat layer and other aspects of the accompanying landscape will slowly disappear. But this is a slow process, and government policies and private initiatives are aimed at preserving this unique landscape for many years to come.

Public Policies and Incentives

- **Spatial planning.** Landscape considerations have guided urbanisation in the region since the 1960s. Recently, the Green Heart was designated as one of 20 Dutch National Landscape areas, but the practical effects of this status are still uncertain.
- **Financial and conservation incentives.** The European Union's Less Favoured Areas (LFA) scheme has been applied to peat areas since the late 1970s, providing modest compensation for farmers facing 'natural handicaps'. Since the 1980s, agri-environment schemes have been in place, with an emphasis on conservation of grassland birds and significant plants species along the numerous watercourses. About 75 per cent of the grassland area in the Green Heart is now covered by one of these programmes. In 2004, authorities decided to expand the LFA scheme in the Green Heart and to increase the budget for agri-environment support.

Private Initiatives

- **Regional produce.** A small number of farms produce Green Heart-branded organic milk and cheese for the regional market. It is also quite common for farmers to sell homemade cheese directly from their farms.
- **Rural tourism.** A small but increasing number of farms in this region supplement their income by offering bed-and-breakfast accommodations or small-scale camping facilities.

The Northern Great Plains of North America

The Northern Great Plains region of the United States and Canada encompasses portions of half a dozen US states and Canada's three prairie provinces of Saskatchewan, Manitoba, and Alberta. While much of this region is normally dry, the area includes millions of tiny wetlands known as 'prairie potholes'. These depressions in the landscape remained when the Ice Age glaciers retreated north. Each spring they replenish themselves with snowmelt and early season rains. Some prairie pothole marshes are temporary, while others are permanent. In those that are year-round, a pattern of rough concentric circles develops. Submerged and floating aquatic plants take over the deeper water in the middle of the pothole while bulrushes and cattails grow closer to shore.

The Prairie Pothole Region is unlike any other landscape in North America, supporting the highest densities of breeding waterfowl on the continent. With its numerous shallow lakes and marshes, rich soils, and warm summers, it is considered one of the most important waterfowl breeding areas in the world. Although this region accounts for only 10 per cent of the available breeding habitat for waterfowl, it can account for greater than 50 per cent of annual continental duck production.

In addition to its hydrological and biological uniqueness, this region is also one of the most productive farming regions in North America. Wheat, barley, sunflowers, soybeans, corn, canola and other small grains grown here are shipped all over the world. Roughly 90 per cent of the US crop of durum pasta wheat and hard red spring wheat are grown in this region. Livestock also play an important role in the agricultural sector of the economy. Between the United States and Canada, more than 27.5 million head of cattle, sheep and hogs help support an extensive livestock industry.

From the time of the European settlers' arrival over a century ago, agriculture has been the primary way of life for the people of this region. Typical family farm sizes range from 150 hectares in north-central Iowa to 500 hectares in Saskatchewan, with some farms as large as several thousand hectares. In the Prairie Pothole Region, there are more than 52 million hectares of land under crop production, capable of producing over $10 billion (US) in crop receipts annually. Coal mining and oil production also help support the region's economy.

Many farms, both large and small, have been hard hit by a combination of economic difficulties and climatic instability. The resulting elimination of numerous family farms in this region has led to the rapid industrialization of farming, including the draining of a significant percentage of the region's wetlands. This draining of wetlands has multiple negative consequences. In addition to their role in agricultural crop production, wetlands play an important role in flood mitigation, water quality protection, and air quality enhancement. They also provide an

Die Region der Pothole-Prärie gilt als eines der wichtigsten Feuchtgebiete weltweit. Diese Region ist nicht nur als Brutplatz für Wasservögel wichtig, sondern ist auch eines der produktivsten Agrargebiete Nordamerikas.

La región de Prairie Pothole está considerada como uno de los humedales más importantes del mundo. Además de constituir una zona de cría vital para las aves acuáticas, también es una de las áreas agrícolas más productivas de América del norte.

Ces fondrières des Prairies sont considérées comme l'une des plus importantes régions marécageuses au monde. Outre le fait qu'il s'agit d'une zone de reproduction très importante pour les oiseaux aquatiques, c'est l'une des régions agricoles les plus productives d'Amérique du Nord.

This Prairie Pothole Region is considered one of the most important wetland regions in the world. In addition to being a critical breeding ground for waterfowl, it is also one of the most productive farming areas of North America.

array of recreational opportunities including hunting, fishing, and wildlife observation.

The United States government's history of supporting resource conservation efforts goes as far back as the Great Depression era of the 1930s. These policies supported farm families through hardships due to environmental devastations and declining commodity prices, while providing incentives and assistance to protect important agrarian landscapes. To protect what is left of this special prairie pothole landscape, a wide range of national conservation and agricultural policies have been enacted over the last 20 years — including the US Department of Agriculture's (USDA) Conservation Reserve Program (CRP), the Wetlands Reserve Program (WRP), and more recently, the Conservation Security Program. One of the key conservation benefits of these programmes is enhancing wildlife habitat, which has bolstered upland bird, waterfowl, and big game populations. These growing wildlife populations have contributed to increased wildlife-based recreation.

Values and Benefits

- **Wildlife habitat.** The Prairie Pothole Region is home to more than 50 per cent of North America's migratory waterfowl, with many species dependent on the potholes for breeding and feeding. Species from Trumpeter Swans and Canvasback Ducks to Blue-Winged Teal and Gadwalls make the tiny, marshy respites their homes every summer.
- **Preserving short grass prairie.** This region is one of the few places where remnants of native short-grass prairie have survived.
- **Flood mitigation.** Prairie potholes absorb surges of rain, snow melt and floodwaters thereby reducing the risk and severity of downstream flooding.
- **Water quality protection.** Wetlands absorb nutrients and hold sediment that comes off of nearby agricultural fields thereby preventing their deposit in streams and rivers.

Blue-Winged Teal is a common bird of prairie potholes.

Challenges and Threats

- **Urban development**. Many important and highly productive pothole regions have been altered or destroyed due to increased commercial development. Only 40 to 50 per cent of the region's original prairie pothole wetlands remain intact today. Computer models predict that for every one per cent of existing grassland that is lost, a drop of 25,000 ducks may occur in the fall migration.

- **National agricultural policy**. The relatively short timeframe of conservation initiatives in USDA farm programs adds an element of uncertainty to land management decisions both at the farm level and at local planning agencies.

- **Small town survival**. Small businesses that supply family farmers find it challenging to remain viable when large tracts of agricultural lands are idled for USDA environmental incentive programmes. This loss has hastened the demise to many small communities throughout the Prairie Pothole Region.

- **Economic stress**. Declining prices for agricultural commodities — linked to international trade agreements, national legislation, and corporate policies — have pressured some family farmers to industrialize their production practices. This often includes expanding cultivation onto fragile lands and adopting more chemical and energy-intensive practices.

- **Climate change**. The impacts of world-wide industrialization may be increasing the variability of seasonal temperatures and the unpredictability and quantity of precipitation thereby affecting wildlife habitat and the ecology of this food-producing region.

Public Policies and Incentives

- **Conservation incentives**. Provisions of USDA programmes, especially the Conservation Reserve Program (CRP) and Swampbuster prohibitions, reduce the short-term economic pressures on farmers to degrade fragile soils and drain wetlands, thus protecting these special wildlife breeding grounds. CRP provides annual payments for land taken out of cultivation and financial assistance for environmental enhancement efforts like the planting of trees and grasses for wildlife habitat and resource-conserving vegetative covers. Within the Prairie Pothole Region, millions of hectares are enrolled in CRP, which has resulted in great population gains for the region's duck and other wildlife species. A major negative aspect of CRP is the relatively short time frame (10 years) of most of its contracts with landowners. An option for family farmers to extend these contracts to 50 years and the addition of permanent easements could significantly increase their positive ecological impact.
- **Prairie preservation**. Maintaining tracts of native prairie can enhance the success of bird populations on adjacent tracts of CRP land. In the areas of North and South Dakota responsible for the bulk of the Prairie Pothole Region's duck production, about four million hectares of native grasses remain.
- **International negotiation**. Ongoing negotiations between the United States and Canada create the possibility that current trade rules could be amended to include provisions that encourage the deintensification and deindustrialization of farming.

Private Initiatives

- **Recreation**. Bird watching, hunting, fishing and other landscape-based recreational activities are increasingly important sources of income for a number of rural communities in the Prairie Pothole Region. Many farmers have built special shelters that they rent to hunters, charging as much as $100 (US) per hunter per day during hunting season. Bird watching 'blinds' and special trails are becoming more common in even the most remote rural areas. Economists estimate the value of hunting to be about $25 (US) per hectare of land in CRP reserve.
- **Tourism**. Public-private partnerships to promote eco- and landscape-based tourism can significantly enhance income for landowners, small-town businesses and local governments. Local business associations in many small towns have taken the lead on community-wide planning that has resulted in major increases in tourism and recreational spending in rural areas. As North Americans become increasingly urbanized, rural experiences become more novel, and nature-based tourism will increasingly be valued to reconnect city dwellers to the land.

Interview with Frederick Kirschenmann

Fred Kirschenmann's family farm near Medina, North Dakota is in the middle of the Prairie Pothole Region. Fred returned to his family farm after his father retired and has developed this nearly 1500 hectare farming operation into one of the best examples of balancing social and biological values with commercial farming and livestock production. Kirschenmann has developed an intricate annual crop rotational system based on ten cash crops and two soil-restoring legumes. One of the most important influences on this thinking and farming is noted North American conservationist Aldo Leopold.

"I first read (Leopold) when I was a junior in college in 1955 and was absolutely blown away by it. At the core of Leopold's understanding was that all of the earth is a community. He referred to it as 'the biotic community', and he felt that one of the major challenges facing us was to find our place in the community rather than being controllers of the land."

Kirschenmann has applied this thinking to his farm. For example, most of his fields are 20 hectares or less and separated by native habitat. "The leguminous plants provide excellent cover for nesting birds early in the spring." His farm is designed so that there is some habitat available at all times. Although he converted his farm to organic many years ago he is clear about the need to re-think this approach in light of new knowledge and changing economic conditions.

In regards to the many challenges facing producers Fred summarizes his thinking in this way: "Organic agriculture must begin to reinvent itself in terms of landscape ecologies. If we are to be successful as organic farmers, long term, we cannot ignore the intricate and complex ecological processes of nature that sustain the whole local ecosystems of which our farms are a part. At the same time, we can begin to similarly restore wild areas and sustainably harvest organic products from them."

Kirschenmann, who also serves as the Executive Director of the Leopold Center for Sustainable Agriculture at Iowa State University, is cautiously optimistic in the face of the many difficulties he sees: "The more our agricultural regions become denuded of their wildlife, the more the farmers will recognize the value of it. The pollinators may be the species that turn the tide. Pollinators are absolutely critical to agriculture. Once farmers realize that they are going to have to create habitat to attract the pollinators, change is going to happen. Then they will have the basis for creating a different kind of consciousness."

The Biebrza River Valley of Poland

The Biebrza River is about 156 kilometres long from its source near the border with Belarus to where it flows into the Narew River. It is surrounded by moraine plateaus formed during the glacial period. The river periodically floods the adjacent lands, generating many different land use patterns across the region. The river valley consists of three main basins, with agricultural lands found mainly in the middle and lower basins. The river and its floodplains offer a spectacular landscape of natural, semi-natural and cultivated habitats.

In 1993, Poland established its largest national park in this area, encompassing almost 60,000 hectares. The park's rich variety of landscapes includes a mosaic of mires, fens, raised bogs, meadows, pastures, natural birch forest, pine forest, and swampy alder forest. Up to 30 per cent of the park can be used for farming, but only 10 to 20 per cent has been farmed in recent years because of the wetness of the meadows.

For many centuries, agriculture has played an important role in the valley. Lands suitable for farming have been grazed by cattle and horses and mown for hay, thus helping to keep the landscape open and preventing encroachment by shrubs and forest. Hay is harvested once or twice a year in the summer. Due to the wet conditions, hay was traditionally harvested by hand, removing the hay in winter when the frozen soil enabled transport by wagon. Now that hand mowing is no longer profitable, the wettest areas remain unmown and the drier areas are mown mechanically. To graze their cattle, farmers ferry the animals across the waters of the Biebrza or have them swim across the river. Many of the herds are so small that they are still milked by hand in the field.

In recent years, some modernisation has taken place. Hand mowing and milking have been partially replaced by their mechanical counterparts, but these adaptations are hampered by the poor revenues of dairy farming. Closing the farm is a more common practice than investing in modernisation.

Der Fluss Biebrza in Polen bietet ein wahres Mosaik aus überschwemmtem, nassem und feuchtem Weideland, Sümpfen und Wäldern und spiegelt die Symbiose aus herkömmlicher Landwirtschaft und damit einhergehenden seltenen Vogelarten wie dem Wachtelkönig, dem Weißstorch und dem Schwarzstorch wieder.

En Polonia, el río Biebrza ofrece un mosaico de prados, zonas pantanosas y bosques inundados y húmedos y muestra una simbiosis de agricultura tradicional y raras especies de aves como el guión de codornices y la cigüeña blanca y negra.

La Biebrza, en Pologne, offre une mosaïque de pâtures inondées et humides, de marais et de forêts naturelles, reflet d'une symbiose d'agriculture traditionnelle, accompagnée d'espèces d'oiseaux rares, comme le râle des genêts et la cigogne blanche et noire.

The Biebrza river valley in Poland offers a mosaic of flooded, wet and moist grasslands, marshes and woodland and reflects a symbiosis of traditional farming with rare bird species like the Corncrake and the White and Black Stork.

Values and Benefits

- **Wildlife habitat**. The Biebrza River valley is famous for its breeding and migrating birds. Over 275 species have been recorded, with 180 species actively breeding. Birds that live in wet meadows include the globally endangered Aquatic Warbler and important species like the Great Snipe, Corncrake, Ruff, Redshank, White and Black Storks, and Crane. This area attracts many European bird watchers.

- **Landscape**. The valley offers spectacular floodplain views which have become rare in Europe.

Die Landwirtschaft befindet sich unter einem starken Druck. Das traditionelle Mähen per Hand ist auf den sehr nassen Weideflächen erforderlich, ist aber sehr zeitaufwendig und wirft kaum Gewinn ab. Die Weideflächen werden daher aufgegeben, wodurch die Landschaft immer monotoner wird. Maschinell betriebenes Mähen ist investitionsintensiv und ist eine Möglichkeit für nur geringfügig nasses Weideland.

La agricultura se encuentra amenazada. En los prados muy húmedos es necesario cortar la hierba manualmente, pero esta tarea requiere mucho tiempo y resulta poco rentable. Por eso están siendo abandonados y el paisaje se va volviendo cada vez más monótono. Para cortar la hierba mecánicamente es necesario invertir en maquinaria y sólo resulta una opción viable en los prados poco húmedos.

L'agriculture est soumise à une rude pression. Le fauchage traditionnel à la main est nécessaire dans les pâturages très humides mais il demande du temps et rapporte peu. En conséquence, les pâtures sont laissées à l'abandon et le paysage devient plus monotone. Le fauchage mécanique nécessite des investissements et n'est possible que dans les pâturages moins humides.

Farming is under pressure. Traditional hand-mowing is needed on the very wet grasslands, but is time-consuming and hardly profitable. As a result, grasslands are being abandoned and the landscape is becoming more monotonous. Mechanical mowing requires investments and is only an option for slightly wet grasslands.

Challenges and Threats

- **Decline in agriculture**. Dairy farming is in rapid retreat in the Bierbza River valley due to increasing technical demands and dairy revenues that are insufficient to allow investment in modern milking and mowing equipment.
- **Decrease in land farmed**. About half of the land in this region is privately owned, most of it by farmers. Increasing amounts of agricultural land are being abandoned because grassland management is time consuming (i.e.many meadows are too wet to be mowed mechanically), the economic returns are poor, the farmers are ageing and most farms are too small to be profitable. There are currently about 17,000 land owners, most of them living outside the Park at a distance of 10 to 20 kilometres from their land, which creates high transportation costs. Within the Park, there are a limited and decreasing number of small farms — the average farm has just seven cows. This reflects a national problem: the total number of cattle in Poland has dropped by 30 per cent over the past decade.
- **Homogenization of the landscape**. As a result of the decline in farming and herd management, parts of the grassland are becoming overgrown by shrubs and trees. The formerly mosaic-like land use pattern is becoming more monotonous, leading to a loss of biodiversity.

Public Policies and Incentives

- **Protected status**. The Biebrza River valley was designated a Landscape Park in 1989 and a National Park in 1993. It has also been proclaimed a RAMSAR Site (Wetlands of International Importance) and a Natura 2000 site under the European Union's Birds Directive. Preparations are being made to submit the region and its adjacent areas for designation as a Unesco Biosphere Reserve and, subsequently, a World Heritage Site.
- **Agri-environment pilot programme**. The first proposal for an agri-environment programme in the country was developed in 1997 in the context of the 'Green Lungs of Poland' initiative, though it took until 2004 for the programme to come into force under the Rural Development Plan for 2004-2006. The Biebrza Valley has been singled out as part of a zonal agri-environment scheme aimed at biodiversity protection in agricultural areas. It is much too early to assess the effects of this effort.
- **Public awareness.** The World Wildlife Fund is enhancing public awareness of the significance of this region, promoting conversion to organic farming in close co-operation with local stakeholders.

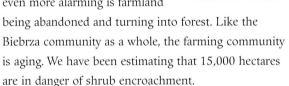

Adam Sieńko, director of the Biebrza National Park: "Low-intensity farming significantly contributes to the Park's biodiversity. We are now facing serious problems including intensification of land use, but even more alarming is farmland being abandoned and turning into forest. Like the Biebrza community as a whole, the farming community is aging. We have been estimating that 15,000 hectares are in danger of shrub encroachment.

The recent agri-environment schemes can be important to maintain farming activities. We try to help where we can. Even before the schemes came into force, the Park was paying landowners for the removal of bushes. With the introduction of the schemes, the Park staff is informing farmers on the management measures, assessing the land that should be eligible most urgently and planning to monitor the scheme's results."

UPLANDS & MOUNTAINS

High altitudes and steep slopes are part of the world's most appealing landscapes. On the one hand, the steep terrain, limited accessibility and often harsh climate protect mountainous landscapes from being intensively utilised. On the other hand, these factors limit the options for active management in situations where such management is required, such as maintaining grasslands that contribute to the landscape and its values. In this chapter, we consider 'upland farming' — farming up to several hundreds of metres above sea level — and genuine mountain farming that occurs at elevations up to thousands of metres high.

The United Kingdom, where hilly regions are common, provides many examples of upland farming. These areas are famous for their low-intensity livestock farming that helps sustain beautiful landscapes, biodiversity and a rich cultural heritage.

Mountain farming is still quite common in Europe, though decreasing in scale over time. The dominant agricultural use in mountain areas is grassland, with rotational and permanent crops playing an important role in some regions. Usually the higher, more remote and steeper slopes are used for grazing — as cattle can graze where machinery cannot be safely used. However, even some very steep slopes can be mown, either with specialised machinery or by hand. The latter is still important in some areas, but is slowly dying out. Extensive livestock grazing systems can still be found in important mountain areas:

- the Alps (France, Switzerland, Italy, Germany, Austria, Slovenia);
- the Pyrenees (France, Spain);
- the Carpathians (Czech and Slovak Republics, Poland, Romania, Moldova).

In addition, many individual countries including Italy, Greece, Croatia, Serbia and Montenegro and the Northern Scandinavian regions contain partly farmed mountain areas. This chapter presents examples from the French and the Slovenian Alps.

The North American landscape has many examples of farming and grazing at all altitudes, from the low mountain ranges of the Appalachians to the high altitude pastures in the Canadian and US Rocky Mountains. The western slopes of the Cascadian Mountain range, extending from northern California up to British Columbia, have some of the most productive farmland in the world. For this chapter we draw on an example from one of the oldest mountain ranges in North America, the Catskills in northeastern New England.

Across Europe and North America

Uplands: the Pennine Dales

Uplands are generally characterised by land at altitudes above 200 metres, topographically and geologically unsuited to intensive cultivation. They cover about 40 per cent of the UK's farmed area, including much of the northern part of England (the Pennines and the Lake District), Wales (Snowdonia and the Cambrian Mountains) and the northern and western parts of Scotland. They contain the largest amount of semi-natural pasture and heathland habitat remaining in the country, most of which is still maintained by low-intensity sheep grazing. Locally, livestock densities can be relatively high and overgrazing by sheep can occur. In valleys and on lower slopes, enclosed grasslands are used for mowing and grazing.

In England, 22 areas have been designated under the Environmentally Sensitive Areas (ESA) scheme introduced in 1987. The Pennine Dales ESA extends over 46,500 hectares of the enclosed upper reaches of 26 valleys (dales). The upland climate can be harsh with high rainfall and a short growing season. The region has extensive areas that are very sparsely populated.

Although each dale has its own character, there is a strong unifying pattern of enclosure created by the traditional drystone walls and numerous stone-built field barns. The enclosure patterns also vary according to their origin; the oldest small-scale field patterns date back to the Bronze or Iron Age. As the dales open out into wider, more fertile valleys, the walls are replaced by hedges. A beautiful tapestry of meadows and pastures, this ESA contains the greatest concentration of traditionally managed meadows and pastures in England.

Present-day farming in this region is based largely on hill sheep and to a lesser extent suckler and store cattle with some dairying. The agricultural system depends heavily on the relatively productive enclosed grassland. Since the 1970s, the traditionally managed grasslands have come increasingly under pressure from intensification (haymaking being replaced by silage) and from increased, but less varied grazing (mixed sheep and cattle systems being replaced solely by sheep).

Aufgrund der schwierigen Produktionsumstände und den ernsten wirtschaftlichen Konsequenzen des Ausbruchs der Maul- und Klauenseuche im Jahr 2001 nimmt die Weidelandfläche ab. Man geht davon aus, dass die CAP-Reform (die Umwandlung von Prämienzahlungen für Tiere in Pauschalbereichszahlungen) diesen Prozess beschleunigen wird.

Debido a la dificultad de este tipo de producción y a las graves consecuencias económicas del brote de fiebre aftosa ocurrido en el 2001, el pasto de montaña está en declive. Se espera que la reforma de la PAC (que convierte las ayudas por animal en ayudas únicas por explotación) no haga sino acelerar este proceso.

En raison des conditions difficiles de production et des graves conséquences économiques de l'épidémie 2001 de fièvre aphteuse, le pâturage en montagne est en régression. On s'attend à ce que la réforme de la PAC (conversion des primes animales en paiements forfaitaires par zone) accélère le processus.

As a result of the difficult production circumstances and the severe economic consequences of the 2001 outbreak of Foot and Mouth Disease, upland grazing is in decline. It is expected that the CAP reform (conversion of animal premia to flat-rate area payments) will accelerate this process.

Values and Benefits

- **Biodiversity**. Notwithstanding the changes, the grasslands still contain a wide diversity of flora and fauna and provide an important habitat for ground-nesting birds. Typical upland hay meadow flora include species such as Devil's Bit Scabious, Wood Cranesbill, Marsh Marigold and Bugle. Meadows and rough pasture support a wide range of associated fauna. Species like the Red Grouse, Peregrine Falcon and Raven attain higher concentrations in the UK uplands than in any other European country. Other notable bird species are Merlin, Golden Plover, Hen Harrier, Curlew and Twite. Several sites in this region have been designated under the EU Birds and Habitats Directives.

- **Cultural significance**. North Yorkshire boasts 60,000 sites of cultural and archaeological importance. The Yorkshire and Humber region as a whole has 56,000 kilometres of stone walls, 50 per cent of England's total. The majority of these sites require active management.

Die Hochweiden in Großbritannien werden gemäht (die niedriger gelegenen, eingeschlossenen Weiden) und von Schafen und Rindern abgeweidet. Die Hochweiden besitzen dennoch eine reiche Artenvielfalt und sind berühmt für Arten wie der Wald-Storchschnabel (Geranium sylvaticum) in den Heuwiesen oder das Schottische Moorschneehuhn im Moorland.

Los prados de las tierras altas del Reino Unido sirven de pasto a ovejas y ganado, con lo que se consigue mantener recortada la hierba de las zonas valladas situadas en las cotas más bajas. Estos prados aún son ricos en biodiversidad, además de ser conocidos por la presencia de especies como el geranio de bosque (Geranium sylvaticum) de los campos de heno y el lagópodo escocés de los páramos.

Les pâturages de montagne, au Royaume-Uni, sont fauchés (terres du bas, clôturées). Des moutons et du bétail y paissent. Ils sont encore riches en biodiversité et connus pour abriter des espèces telles le géranium des bois (Geranium sylvaticum), dans les prairies de fauche et le lagopède d'Écosse, dans les tourbières.

Upland grasslands in the UK are mown (the lower, enclosed parts) and grazed by sheep and cattle. They are still rich in biodiversity and famous for species like Wood Cranesbill in the hay meadows and Red Grouse on the moorland.

Challenges and Threats

- **Land deterioration**. In some areas, intensification has lead to overgrazing by sheep. This has been enhanced by 'headage' or per animal payments — such as the ewe premium.

- **Decreased grazing diversity**. In large parts of the area, the replacement of cattle by sheep (which results in less varied grazing patterns) is seen as a major threat. With the replacement of headage payments by area payments, this lack of grazing diversity could be compounded by undergrazing or even land abandonment. As the farmed grasslands are vital to the region's biodiversity and cultural and historical features, a decline in farming would affect more than just the farming community.

- **Health issues**. The 1986 BSE (Mad Cow) outbreak followed by the 2001 outbreak of Foot and Mouth Disease accelerated the migration of labour from agriculture. During the Foot and Mouth outbreak, a large part of the area was closed to the public, which had a substantially negative effect on rural tourism. Recent farm reports show a slow recovery of income, but the situation is still at an unsustainable level with many farming families in the region reliant upon non-agricultural income. In remote and sparsely populated areas (e.g. North Yorkshire), agriculture still accounts for a substantial share of employment and alternative employment for farm workers is limited.

Public Policies and Incentives

- **Compensatory payments**. The UK established a special national policy for the uplands in the mid-1940s, aiming to maintain hill farming by compensating producers who faced difficult production circumstances. All the land within the Pennine Dales ESA is classified by the European Union as having a Less Favoured Areas (LFA) status — a large share of the almost ten million hectares of LFA land in the UK. In these areas farmers can claim compensatory payments. In the past, compensatory payments and headage payments were regarded as the most stable portion of the hill farmers income, at times accounting for up to half of the net farm income on LFA holdings.

- **Conservation schemes**. Since the early 1990s, the UK has been implementing a number of comprehensive environmental and conservation schemes, of which the ESA scheme and the Countryside Stewardship Scheme (CSS) are the most important. In the Pennines, large areas have management agreements under one or both of these schemes. ESA monitoring has shown that under such agreements plant and bird species of low-intensity grasslands are fairly stable and that most of the landscape's, archaeological and historic features have been maintained.

- **Impacts of changes**. It is expected that the recently reformed EU support regime (from animal payments to flat-rate area payments not connected to grazing) will raise the problem of undergrazing in the uplands, especially as far as suckler cows are concerned. For some habitats, active grazing will no longer be a criterion for support, as long as the land management complies with good farming and environmental standards.

Mountains: the Alps

In Europe there are 29 countries with mountains, encompassing, on average, 40 per cent of their land. In these countries, almost 20 per cent of the total population lives in these mountainous regions. The dominant agricultural area in such mountain areas is grassland, with arable (row) crops playing an important role in some regions. There are also permanent crops, like olive groves, vineyards, and fruit orchards, that are important in a number of local areas. Here we present examples of mountain farming from two national parks in the Alps.

Mountain farming is associated with hard work, but also with species-rich grasslands. Notable plant species, for instance in Les Écrins National Park, are the Alpine Sea Holly (photo above) and several orchid species. Mountain grasslands represent a delicate balance between farming and nature, which is under increasing pressure.

Die Berglandwirtschaft wie hier in den Alpen ist relativ kostspielig wegen der zeitaufwendigen Arbeit oder der besonderen Investitionen wie beispielsweise in Mähen an Steilhängen. Die wirtschaftlichen Perspektiven verschlechtern sich mit fallenden Milch- und Fleischpreisen. Es gibt Initiativen zur Entwicklung spezieller Bergprodukte (mit einer "Herkunftsbescheinigung"), die zu einem höheren Preis verkauft werden.

Aquí en los Alpes, la agricultura de montaña resulta relativamente costosa debido al tiempo que requiere o a sus necesidades especiales, por ejemplo cortar la hierba de empinadas laderas. Las perspectivas económicas se reducen al mismo ritmo que los precios de la leche y la carne. Existen iniciativas para desarrollar productos especiales de montaña (con un "certificado de origen") que se venden a un precio más alto.

L'agriculture en montagne, ici dans les Alpes, est relativement coûteuse en raison du travail exigeant beaucoup de temps ou des investissements spéciaux, par exemple quand il s'agit de faucher les pentes abruptes. Les perspectives économiques sont moins bonnes, avec la chute des prix du lait et de la viande. Des initiatives sont en cours, visant à mettre au point des produits montagnards spécifiques (avec "certificat d'origine"), vendus à un prix plus élevé.

Mountain farming, here in the Alps, is relatively costly due to time-consuming work or special investments, e.g. equipment to mow steep slopes. Economic perspectives are decreasing, as milk and meat prices are falling. There are initiatives to develop special mountain products (with a 'certificate of origin'), sold at a higher price.

Les Écrins National Park in the French Alps

The Les Écrins National Park was established in 1973 and includes an area of almost 92,000 hectares, located at altitudes between 800 and 4,100 metres. One-third of the park, mainly alpine grasslands, is used by farmers. In 1995 there were some 750 farmers, almost half of them specialising in sheep farming, 15 per cent in dairy farming and another 15 per cent in beef cattle farming.

The Park has abundant biodiversity: 1,800 plant species and 320 vertebrate fauna species have been recorded. The grasslands significantly contribute to this diversity, hosting important plant species like Alpine Sea Holly and Poet's Narcissus and birds such as Red-backed Shrike, Common Quail, Corncrake, and Winchat.

Because of the difficult production circumstances and the ageing of the farming community, the number of farmers is dropping rapidly, by almost one-quarter every ten years. An increasing number of alpine meadows are being abandoned due to poor access or small size. To slow down abandonment, the government has been investing in pastoral facilities such as access roads, huts and water supplies. However, many farmers rely heavily on additional income from tourism. As the park welcomes one million visitors every year, tourism is a promising market. In 1998, the Park and the regional Chamber of Agriculture signed an agreement on environmentally-sound farming practices, labelling of mountain products and further cooperation. In the framework of an EU co-financed project, the facilities for rural tourism are now being improved, hand in hand with the maintenance of traditional farming.

Agri-environment programmes have been helping to slow the loss of farmers and to protect farmland biodiversity. About three-quarters of the region's farmers have applied for mountain support under the Less Favoured Areas scheme. In addition, over 25,000 hectares of grasslands have been contracted under the French farmland conservation scheme CTE (*Contrat Territoriale d'Exploitation*). This scheme was replaced by a different one in 2002, which is considered to be less suitable for mountain farming than the foregoing scheme.

Interview with Pierre-Yves Motte

Pierre-Yves Motte, the farmers' president in the National Park: "The farmers in the Park devote their knowledge and practices to the natural and cultural richness of the mountain massif. About one-third of the park area is being farmed and the farmland substantially contributes to the beauty of the typical middle-mountain countryside with terraces and hedges. Together with tourism, agriculture plays an important role in the liveability of our valleys. Now, with the way the farming society and the farm support systems are developing, the survival of a sufficient number of farms strongly depends on economic innovation and diversification, like rural tourism and regional produce. The recognition and remuneration of the farmers' role in nature conservation might also be an important, although secondary, contribution to economic sustainability."

Im Nationalpark "Les Écrins" in den französischen Alpen geht die Zahl der Landwirte rapide zurück. Infolgedessen wird eine immer größere Anzahl an Feldern aufgegeben und überwachsen. Spezielle Unterstützungsaktionen helfen zwar, können diese Entwicklung letztendlich aber nicht aufhalten.

En el parque nacional de Les Écrins, en los Alpes franceses, el número de granjeros se reduce rápidamente. Por eso cada vez hay más campos descuidados y abandonados. Los programas de ayudas especiales son útiles, pero no consiguen frenar esta tendencia.

Dans le Parc National des Écrins des Alpes françaises, le nombre d'agriculteurs est en diminution croissante. Conséquence : un nombre de plus en plus important de champs sont laissés à l'abandon et retournent à la friche. Si les programmes d'aide spéciaux ont une certaine utilité, ils ne parviennent pas à mettre fin à cette évolution.

In Les Écrins National Park in the French Alps, the number of farmers is decreasing rapidly. As a result an increasing number of fields are abandoned and overgrown. Special support schemes help, but are hardly able to stop this development.

Triglav National Park
in the Julian Alps, Slovenia

Triglav National Park is situated in the northwestern part of Slovenia, bordering Italy and Austria. It encompasses 84,000 hectares, mainly limestone, rising up to almost 3,000 metres at mount Triglav. It is famous for its deep gorges and impressive waterfalls. Since 1924, a small area has been legally protected; the park's current boundaries were established in 1981.

There are 400 agricultural holdings in the park, of which only 10 per cent are full-time and of substantial size. One-third of the farms take in additional income from rural tourism, cheesemaking or off-farm jobs. The rest of the farms are semi-subsistence farms. Bohinj, with a concentration of alpine meadows, has for centuries been Slovenia's dairy centre, with herds migrating up and down the mountains. Farming really started to flourish after the introduction of cooperative cheese-making in the late 19th century. The typical hayrack (kazolec in Slovenian) has become part of the country's cultural heritage. When a modern dairy factory was opened outside the area in 1971, dairy farming and cheesemaking started to decline.

Over recent decades, limited access, steep slopes, depopulation and abandonment have been leading to serious management problems in the region: about one-third of the grasslands have become overgrown. Today, 60 alpine pastures are still being managed. The farmers cooperate to process milk and market their dairy products.

Slovenia possesses rich semi-natural grassland vegetations, including many rare and endemic species. In the National Park, the wet grasslands and sedge vegetations include plant species like Verticillate Lousewort, Clusius Gentian, Alpine Pasqueflower and the endemic Julian Lousewort and Triglav Gentian. Farmland animals include the Alpine Ibex, Chamois and the Apollo butterfly. The entire park has been designated as a Natura 2000 area.

Slovenia started a national agri-environment scheme in 2001, before its accession to the EU, with Triglav as a pilot region. The schemes include a remarkable range of well-tailored measures for the restoration of overgrown meadows and the conservation of biodiversity and landscape features. Other policy incentives include support for modernisation of dairy farms and the development of regional trademarks.

Values and Benefits

- **Biodiversity**. High-altitude grasslands are renowned for their biodiversity. In particular, the flora of extensively used grasslands can be very rich. A study of the Alps' agricultural genetic resources showed that there are more than a hundred endangered livestock breeds and numerous unique plant varieties.

- **Culture and community**. Mountain farming is also special for the ways it contributes to social and cultural activities: in the often very small and remote villages, communities live together in a small-scale and strongly interrelated economy, keeping up traditional feasts related to, for example, harvesting or transhumance.

Challenges and Threats

- **High costs, low productivity**. Relatively high production costs due primarily to low productivity that results from the harsh climate, long distances, poor accessibility, high costs of infrastructure and specialised equipment, and time-consuming harvesting. For example some hay harvesting is still done by hand.
- **Abandonment of grasslands**. The number of cows sent out to summer pastures is declining, and as a result, part of the grassland has been abandoned and is becoming overgrown. This trend dramatically affects the biodiversity in these areas.
- **Declining agricultural base**. Conversion from dairy cattle to sucklers is weakening agriculture's economic base. Without dairy farming, the management of mountain grasslands becomes too expensive.
- **Population loss**. In an increasing number of areas, low and decreasing population densities lead to the slow disappearance of settlement structures and cultural heritage.
- **Globalisation**. It is expected that as a result of increasing globalisation and the revised EU support schemes, the existing regional disparities in agriculture will be aggravated. In high altitudes, this will accelerate the abandonment process, thus endangering both the rich ecosystem of meadows and pastures and the varied cultural landscape. .

Public Policies and Incentives

- **Need for focused policies**. Policies for mountain farming are often embedded in broader, integrated policies for sustainable development of mountain areas: regional policy, economic development (tourism, infrastructure) and/or environmental policy. Since the 1980s, there have been pleas for a more coherent EU mountain policy, but thus far problems specific to mountains have been addressed with traditional policy measures. As the French and Slovenian examples show, these include Less Favoured Areas support, farmland conservation schemes and EU programmes for rural development. Evaluations show some improvement in terms of economic diversification and conservation, but mountain populations keep declining and unemployment remains high.
- **Roles of national and regional authorities**. On the one hand, the recent CAP reform (de-coupling support from production) is perceived as a serious threat for the maintenance of remote farmland. On the other hand, the rural development budgets will increase and national governments will have more opportunities to redistribute and target the support. The future of mountain farming is therefore strongly in the hands of national and regional authorities.

Private Initiatives

Some existing policy measures encourage private initiatives for mountain farming, such as:

- **International co-operation and agreements** (e.g. Alpine and Carpathian Conventions). The Alpine Convention contains a protocol on agriculture (adopted in 1994), which includes agreements on environmentally-sound land use, conservation of wildlife and genetic resources, production and marketing of regional products and improvement of livelihood and working conditions.
- **Strategic product labelling**. Product labelling can be used to increase revenues, like in the French project 'From the Mountains'. Under the 1992 EU regulation on quality labels, mountains were designated as an official region of origin in 2000, providing better opportunities for marketing.

The Catskill Mountains of New York

While North America is comparatively rich in terms of ground and surface water resources and average rainfall, the challenges of protecting this water and sharing it equitably between and among the competing demands of agriculture, industry, urban dwellers, tourists, wildlife and nature are now a central element in many local, state and federal agricultural policies. No place better illustrates this than the ancient mountainous region called the Catskills, just 160 kilometres north of New York City.

Encompassing more than 6,000 square miles of mountains, forests, rivers and farmland, the Catskills are often referred to as America's First Wilderness, because scholars trace the beginnings of the environmental conservation movement to this beautiful area. With almost three dozen mountain peaks reaching as high as 1,110 vertical metres and six major river systems, the Catskills are an ecological resource of significant importance.

The Catskills are covered by a wide range of northern hardwood tree species, including Maple, Yellow Birch, and American Beech, along with White Ash, Cherry, Red Oak, Hemlock, and White Pine. In the eastern Catskill region, along the edge of the Hudson Valley, the dominant species are Red Oak, Chestnut Oak, Hickory, White and Pitch Pine. Wild berries, including blueberries and huckleberries, are also prevalent in this region. Several of the tallest Catskill Mountains are capped with Red Spruce and Balsam Fir. There are also many swamps, bogs, wetlands, and river valleys with distinct communities of species throughout the entire mountain range. Slopes in the Catskills range from nearly flat areas along the larger river valleys, to nearly

vertical cliffs. Ravines with steep slopes may be covered with both large trees and delicate ferns.

Farming has always played an important role in these mountains. The Catskills are home to over 500 farms, offering a wide variety of food and forestry products. Dairy farming has been a mainstay, particularly in the northeastern portion of the Catskills, but it has been declining in recent years. In contrast, fruit orchards and wineries are growing in number in some parts of the region. With changes in consumer demands, more farmers have moved to sustainable and alternative agricultural production, including organics, specialty produce, and humane animal production.

Thanks to the distinctive geological formations in this region, it is ideal for capturing and channelling large quantities of fresh water — a gift from nature that the city fathers of New York recognized very early on. Over the last 100 years, the region has been dominated by the pull of water to New York City. The Catskills landscape, supplying nearly 90 per cent of the drinking water for New York City's population of 10 million people, comes from the snow and rain that falls on these mountains, flowing unfiltered through a system of rivers, reservoirs, and pipelines year-round.

About 15 years ago, health officials began to worry about the possible contamination of this water with run-off from the small farms, mostly dairy farms, that dotted the mountainsides and

Die Farmer in den Catskill Mountains von Neuengland tragen dazu bei, die Wasserversorgung der Stadt New York zu unterstützen, indem sie bestimmte Vorgehensweisen zum Schutz des Wassers auf ihrem Land einführen.

Los granjeros de las montañas Catskill, en Nueva Inglaterra, ayudan a proteger el suministro de agua de la ciudad de Nueva York gracias al uso de métodos de conservación en sus tierras.

Les agriculteurs des montagnes de Catskill en Nouvelle Angleterre veillent à la sauvegarde des réserves d'eau de New York City en appliquant des mesures de protection de la nature sur leurs terres.

Farmers in the Catskill Mountains of New England help protect New York City's water supply by implementing conservation practices on their land.

valleys of the Catskills, as well as the increased urban development in the region. Under the constitution of the state of New York, the city government has the legal authority to do anything to protect the city's water. They were of two minds. Some wanted to shut down all the farms left in this region and turn the land into a protected area with limited public access. Others, including Al Appleton, a visionary city commissioner in charge of the water system at that time, knew that eliminating the farms was not the right approach. "We eliminated farmers in other regions and suddenly found the land covered with roads, housing, shopping malls, parking lots and other kinds of suburban development that resulted in very bad environmental problems. At the end of the day, we knew it would be best to keep the families on the land, but we had to find a way to do this that was both economically and ecologically sustainable over time."

Appleton and his team began working with the association of farmers that came together in the Catskills region, called the Watershed Agricultural Council (WAC), to develop a comprehensive plan. It called for changes in farming practices on nearly all of the farms in this catchment region that were to be financially supported by all levels of government — local, state and federal.

The centerpiece of this historic agreement was the idea of 'whole farm planning' — an approach that works with each farm individually to determine what changes can be made to the farm to provide the most benefit to the environment, farm income, and quality of life of the farm family. Funds for implementing a Whole Farm Plan were provided by the state government via the extension services of the land grant university. The costs of implementing the changes spelled out in the plans were to be shared by the city water consumers and the federal government through a 'cost-sharing' program.

While this Whole Farm Planning approach did an excellent job of transforming the farming practices to protect the water supply, it was less successful in ensuring the financial sustainability of the families who were farming. The WAC recognized this fact early on and began to work with government officials to develop additional policies to address the economic challenges. One idea was the development of a special regional label for food products coming from the watershed, backed by a marketing campaign, that urged residents of New York City to "protect your water, buy Catskill products." Federal and state government programs were used to help expand agro-forestry and to develop new specialty crops, such as fingerling potatoes, to help farmers diversify their income streams. Private initiatives, such as Forest Stewardship Council certification of forest management practices, are being explored to further ensure the economic sustainability of this initiative.

Values and Benefits

- **Safe water supply**. Protection of these landscapes helps ensure the supply of safe drinking water for New York City, the largest city in the United States. This is a top priority for policymakers throughout the region because there are no alternative sources.
- **Biodiversity**. These ancient mountains have developed unique habitats where important and unique flora and fauna can thrive. The farms and the livestock they have maintained are crucial to providing the mix of ecological communities needed to sustain this biodiversity.
- **Recreation**. For the more than 20 million people living within a short distance of this region, the green space of these landscapes is a crucial recreational and tourism benefit.

Challenges and Threats

- **Unstable markets**. While government funding for some infrastructure upgrading has been significant, the ongoing financial stability of the farmers in this region depends on an increasingly unstable, global marketplace.
- **Prohibitive costs for new farmers**. The ageing population of operating farmers indicates the need for new entrants into farming, but the capital costs are far greater than conventional business operations can sustain.
- **Urbanisation.** The proximity of this land to New York City makes it vulnerable to urban development. Farmers may find it more lucrative to sell their land than to continue farming.

Public Policies and Incentives

- **Water supply and protection policies**. Water quality protection is becoming a more clearly defined national priority, making it feasible to generate long-term political and public financial support for innovative approaches to drinking water protection, such as protecting farmland.
- **Local policies**. The momentum gained by initiatives taken by farmers and small landowners can be used to motivate small towns to address water quality degradation issues within their jurisdictions.
- **International trade**. International trade rules that now discourage local rural economic development strategies can be reversed in new negotiations to permit affirmative action on the part of local governments to support agrarian landscape protection.

Private Initiatives

- **Improved markets for local food**. Popular restaurants and food markets in nearby cities, including New York, are increasingly purchasing products from local farmers.
- **Rural tourism**. Agri-tourism initiatives by residents of the region have made a significant contribution to the economic stability of the region.
- **Land trusts.** A number of private organisations are working to put farmland in land trusts that protect it from development.

BOREAL LANDSCAPES

Boreal landscapes can be found all around the world, especially in the northern hemisphere. The boreal landscapes of countries such as Scandinavia, Siberia, Canada and the Baltics are renown for their spectacular beauty — a dramatic expanse of coniferous forests, mountain ranges, rolling hills, grasslands, marshes and bogs.

Boreal regions are found at higher latitudes, translating into cool climates with short, warm summers and long, cold winters. Growing seasons and grazing periods are short. Densely populated regions are rare and the long distances between these areas make transportation of goods costly. These factors make

farming in boreal regions difficult. As a result, abandonment of land — mainly grassland — is a widespread phenomenon in areas where farming is no longer profitable. In these areas, the forest encroaches on former farmland and the benefits associated with the farmland are lost. This is a concern to farmers and to conservationists alike since a large part of the biodiversity in these regions is related to farmland.

This chapter looks at examples from Sweden and the Canadian province of British Columbia, as well as from Sami and Alaskan native cultures, to understand the challenges and opportunities for farming in boreal regions.

Sweden: Småland

As more than half of Sweden's 45 million hectares consists of forest and one-third of mountains, marshes and lakes, the agricultural area in Sweden is limited to seven per cent of the land surface (just over three million hectares). The length of the growing season can differ up to 100 days between the very south (Skåne; average temperature 8.4 °C) and the very north (Norrbotten; average temperature — 2.5 °C).

Of the 70,000 Swedish farms, only 20,000 are full-time enterprises. Many farmers combine farming with forestry or some other second job, especially in the mountain and forest regions. For many, farming is their second job. Cropping takes place on 2.7 million hectares, this being the main use of land on the plains in central and southern Sweden. Permanent pastures account for a half million hectares, but dairy farms also use a large share of the crops grown on the areas arable land for fodder. Dairy farming is predominant in the southwest, but also is common in densely forested districts like Småland.

Sweden has for years been coping with environmental problems related to land abandonment. Although Sweden's accession to the EU in 1995 helped to slow down this process, the depletion of the farmed landscape's natural and cultural values is a continuous concern. This problem mainly affects natural pastures that have high conservation values, particularly those in woodland and mixed woodland/flatland areas. In the northern areas and the forested regions of central Sweden, between 10 and 30 per cent of the grasslands (tens of thousands of hectares) are no longer used.

Småland county in southern Sweden is an example of an area affected by a loss of farmland. Småland contains about nine per cent of the Swedish land and population. Of the millions of Swedes that emigrated to North America, about 20 per cent came from here. The main economic sectors in the county are engineering and production industries (like Husqvarna) and woodworking.

In the Middle Ages, Småland was a swampy and lake-rich area where the Vikings produced iron. It is one of Sweden's most forested counties and has an abundance of lakes. The extensive spruce forests have given the county its nickname 'Dark Småland'. The landscape of Småland used to be more open — the spruce forest kept away by burnbeating and grazing. Agriculture was the major economic activity, but the stony moraine soil prevented farmers from cultivating larger areas. However, in the 19th century, many swamps and bogs were drained in order to increase the agricultural area.

The current landscape of Småland is a mixed woodland-farmland landscape with 6.5 times more woodland than farmland. The average farm ratio between pasture, arable land and woodland is 1:2:5. Dairy farms make up 20 per cent of the farms, and while the overall number of farms is continuously decreasing, dairy farms shows an even more rapid drop, 40 per cent since 1995. As the number of dairy cows has dropped, the number of suckler cows has increased. Between 1960 and 1990, one quarter of the arable land in Småland was abandoned. This mainly comprised small and remote fields that had a high content of peat and poor drainage.

Die Landwirtschaft in der dicht bewaldeten Region von Småland ist wegen der klein geschnittenen, bruchstückhaften und steinigen Felder sowie einer kurzen Produktionszeit relativ kostspielig.

En la boscosa región de Småland la agricultura es relativamente costosa debido a los pedregosos y fragmentados campos a pequeña escala y a la reducida duración de la temporada productiva.

L'agriculture, dans la région fortement boisée de Småland est relativement coûteuse en raison de la petite dimension, de la fragmentation et du caractère pierreux des champs ainsi que de la brièveté de la saison de production.

Farming in the densely wooded Småland region is relatively costly due to the small scale, fragmented and stony fields and a short production season.

Values and Benefits

- **Open landscape.** This has become rare.
- **Rich biodiversity.** The farmed area of Smaland is still relatively rich in biodiversity, typical for this mixture of small-scale farmland and forest. On a national level, it has been calculated that roughly 1,700 plant and animal species are associated with farmland.
- **Wildlife.** Mammals found in farmed areas include the Roedeer, Fieldmouse and Hare, and birds such as Lapwing, White Wagtail, Whinchat and Yellowhammer.
- **Plant diversity.** Plant species in and around farmland include Lady's Bedstraw, Lesser Burnet, Common Milkwort, Bluebell, Meadow Vetchling and Globeflower.

The Småland farmland is still rich in biodiversity, with plants like the Meadow Vetchling and birds like the Yellowhammer. But due to the declining farm profitability, the forest is encroaching.

Interview with Sven-Inge Ågren

Sven-Inge Ågren has run a dairy farm in Eksjö, Småland since 1994. His wife, Gunilla, has a job off of the farm. The farm has 55 dairy cows and 60 young cattle, 54

hectares of arable land, 30 hectares of semi-natural meadows and 95 hectares of forest.

"Over the last decade, I have doubled the milk production from the same farmland area and built a new cow shed," he explains. "The possibilities for further modernisation are limited, as my 84 hectares of farmland are scattered over 80 lots, many of them at long distance from the farm."

"We heavily rely on support schemes like Less Favoured Areas, agri-environment and animal premia," he continues. "All 30 hectares of semi-natural meadows are under the agri-environment scheme, as are 39 hectares of arable land. Next to that, we receive payments for conservation of landscape and cultural heritage: ditches, field roads, stone walls, trees, etc. On the long run, these payments will not be able to maintain farming in this area. In my opinion, cattle farming has to be profitable even without these premia. But as the Småland people have a reputation of being stubborn, I think that large parts of the farmed landscape will be maintained in the future as well."

Challenges and Threats

- **Economic viability**. The overall economy of farming is very poor. Due to the low profitability of farming in Småland, along with the promise of harsh work and little social life, few young people are interested in taking over their families' farms. As the farming community ages, there is little hope for next generation replacements. As a result, a growing area of land is being abandoned and taken over by the forest, spontaneously or commercially (afforestation).
- **Declining biodiversity.** Because of the abandonment of farmland, biodiversity in the county is declining. About 20 per cent of the farmland species are now more or less threatened.

Public Policies and Incentives

- **Environmental and Rural Development Plan for Sweden 2000-2006**. This plan, co-financed by the EU, provides the following public incentives which have helped increase the area of well-managed grasslands in Småland.
    - Support for regional development and improvement of infrastructure, co-financed by the EU.
    - Less Favoured Areas (LFA) support because of the danger of depopulation. All of Småland's farmland is eligible.
    - Since 1986, the Swedish government has been supporting the conservation and restoration of valuable grasslands through agri-environment payments. The most important measures are conservation and maintenance of all semi-natural grazing land and mown meadows and maintenance of a varied agricultural landscape and preventing large-scale abandonment of agricultural land in the northern part of Sweden and in the densely forested districts of southern Sweden.

  Participation in LFA and conservation schemes requires active management: mowing or grazing with a certain minimum livestock density.
- **Beef premiums**. The mid-2003 CAP reform (shift from production support to rural development support), partially continues these premiums for a transitional period to 2009 because of their contribution to the environmental goal of a varied agricultural landscape.

The Peace River Valley of British Columbia

In North America, the boreal forest and plains occupy nearly 28 per cent of the land, or 15 million square kilometres — about one-tenth of the earth's northern land surface. This enchanted forest, sometimes referred to as the *taiga*, is incredibly biologically diverse. It features both the largest and smallest of mammals in North America (the Bison and Pygmy Shrew) and is home to the lakes, wild rivers, vast bogs, fens, and other natural wetlands. The boreal forest is by far the largest ecosystem in North America.

Over the past 200 years, new immigrants migrating from Europe to the US and Canada have pushed this forest back to make room for farming and grazing, laying the groundwork for a strong rural economy. In many regions, the rural economy offered opportunities for multiple income streams, as farmers harvested crops in the summer and worked as loggers in the winter. Meanwhile, many animals came to rely on the 'edge' between the forest and farmland as the best place to nest, flourish, and thrive in safe and unique surroundings. One of the places where this balance of wild and cultivated lands can be seen most clearly is in the Peace River Valley of British Columbia, Canada.

Running eastward across Alberta from the confluence of the Finlay and Parsnip Rivers, the nearly 2000-kilometre Peace River has formed a fertile farm region along its course. Within British Columbia, the Peace River Valley includes includes more than 400,000 hectares of farmland, over half of which are used for annual crops, including nearly all of the province's cereal grain and oilseed crops and a significant portion of its forage crops. Although the growing season is very short at this high latitude, the region is surprisingly warm, thanks to the Chinook winds blowing off of the Rocky Mountains to the west and summertime daylight hours of nearly 18 hours. The area's agricultural industry has developed into a highly diversified sector that includes grain and hay production, grass and grass seed production, livestock, honeybees, and game farming of bison, caribou and wild boar.

The Peace River Valley is very diverse in terms of flora and fauna, supporting a wide variety of wildlife. The valley offers some of the best trout habitat in the world, alongside prime calving grounds for elk and moose. While the boreal forest region in North America covers a vast swath of land, the portion that is cultivated remains very small and limited to sub-climates where conditions are ideal for special cropping practices. These farms help to keep some of the landscape open and without forest cover, allowing for a number of unique bird habitats to flourish. Among the birds that need theses open spaces or forest edges for nesting, feeding or breeding are the American Kestrel, Black

Unbebautes Land und Ackerland gibt es gleichermaßen im Peace River Valley von Britisch-Kolumbien (Kanada). Dieses Waldgebiet in der borealen Zone unterstützt verschiedene Landwirtschaftszweige und bildet den Lebensraum für den Amerikanischen Elch, den Bären und viele weitere Arten der Tier- und Pflanzenwelt sowie verschiedene Vogelarten.

En el valle del río Peace, en la Columbia Británica (Canadá), existe un equilibrio entre tierras salvajes y cultivadas. Este paraje boreal soporta una industria agrícola diversa y da cobijo a alces, osos y otros muchos tipos de fauna y aves.

Dans la vallée de la Rivière-de-la-Paix en Colombie britannique, au Canada, terres sauvages et terres cultivées cohabitent. Cette région boréale abrite une industrie agricole variée et est le territoire privilégié des élans, des ours et de bien d'autres types d'espèces animales sauvages ainsi que d'oiseaux.

Wild and cultivated lands exist in a balance in the Peace River Valley of British Columbia, Canada. This boreal region supports a diverse agricultural industry and is home to moose, bear and many other types of wildlife and bird species.

Capped Chickadees, Rufous Hummingbirds and Burrowing Owls.

In addition to the birds and mammals that rely on the open-space created by the farms, other animals living in the region include Grizzly and Black bears, deer, moose, caribou, and Bald Eagles. The distinct climate also supports a wide range of fish, such as Lake Char, Walleye, Arctic Grayling and Rainbow Trout.

Values and Benefits

- **Landscape diversity**. Farming in the boreal region, which is dominated by forests, creates open spaces that provide a more diverse landscape.
- **Biodiversity**. Open spaces created by farms provide unique habitats for animals and plants. Many species, such as the American Kestrel and the Capped Chickadee, rely on the edge created between forests and farmland for habitat.

Challenges and Threats

- **Economic difficulties**. Generally low agricultural prices make it difficult to earn a living farming in this region, leading to the abandonment of land. The expansion of the forest into abandoned farms now threatens the plant and animal species that once flourished in these open spaces.
- **Oil and gas exploration and drilling**. In an effort to find alternatives to low farming income, there has been a push by the government to expand the use of petroleum and natural gas resources. There have been some serious environmental and human health consequences, including major pipeline leaks, that have resulted in major fish kills.
- **Hydroelectric power development**. A proposed new dam on the Peace River would displace dozens of farms through flooding and would destroy a number of cultural heritage sites. Environmentalists worry that the dam would cause river temperatures to rise downstream, which could affect the ability of the region's fish species to survive. First Nations people also worry about the effects on the local moose population.

Public Policies and Incentives

- **Conservation assistance**. Farmers are eligible to receive various forms of conservation assistance from the provincial and federal governments. For instance, the Shelterbelt Program offers free trees and shrubs as a part of its promotion of soil conservation and land reclamation in order to create wildlife habitat, manage snow, stabilize crops and provide opportunities for agroforestry.

Private Initiatives

- **Tourism**. Efforts are underway to attract a wider tourism base and more recreational fishing and hunting visitors to help further diversify the economy.

Reindeer Husbandry: the Sami culture

The indigenous Sami people were living in the northern part of Scandinavia (the former Fennoscandia region) long before national boundaries were drawn. While the Sami, with a current population of 80,000, do not have their own sovereign state — their communities are divided between Norway, Sweden, Finland and the Russian Kola peninsula — they do have their own language, culture and parliament. Of the 20,000 Sami living in Sweden, 3,000 are involved in reindeer farming in the northern parts of the country. Over 230,000 reindeer make up the herds. Most Sami families derive their income from a combination of reindeer husbandry, fishing, hunting and crafts. The Reindeer Husbandry Law (1971) allows the Sami some economic freedom within their communities.

The reindeer is related to other deer species but is uniquely well-adapted to arctic and sub-arctic circumstances. Its hooves are broad, flexible and hairy, enabling it to walk on soft snow in winter, on mosses and swamps in summer, and to dig for food in deep snow. Reindeer can be found across the polar circle (US, Canada, Scandinavia, Russia, Siberia) and even in Mongolia and parts of China. They are able to survive on large parts of the earth's surface that are unsuitable for other kinds of farming. In Alaska and Canada, wild reindeer are called Caribou.

Domestication and breeding of reindeer remain indigenous enterprises. Indigenous cultures rely heavily on reindeer farming for their continued survival. Reindeer are used for transport (to pull sledges) and for their milk, meat and hides (to make tents, shoes and clothes). Today, meat production is the primary economic activity.

Reindeer graze throughout the year. During the short summers, they are herded on the tundra or taiga. In the winter they forage in the forests, eating large amounts of lichen from the ground and from old spruce trees. Although the Sami differ from the Western nations in their concept of territoriality, their herding system is not a nomadic one.

The last decade has brought important innovations to reindeer farming. For example, Sweden and Finland have been establishing reindeer herding districts as for-profit corporations. The reindeer owners are members or shareholders of the cooperative. These districts have strictly defined boundaries, varying in area from 1,000 to 5,000 square kilometres. The number of reindeer in each district is regulated by a county administrative board. Additionally, modern technology has been

Die Haltung von Rentieren ist bereits mehrere tausend Jahre alt und ist überall im Bereich des Polarkreises zu finden. Es handelt sich hierbei um Flächen, die für andere Arten der Landwirtschaft ungeeignet sind. Die Rentierhaltung wird hauptsächlich von den Ureinwohnern betrieben - in Schweden von dem Sami (Lappen) – und ist mit einem speziellen arktischen Erbe an Artenvielfalt und Kultur wie Zäune, Holzbalken usw. verbunden.

La ganadería de renos se remonta a hace miles de años y se desarrolla alrededor de todo el Círculo Polar, en superficies que no son adecuadas para otros tipos de ganadería. Suele ser practicada por los indígenas (en Suecia los samis o lapones), respetando una biodiversidad ártica específica y su herencia cultural (cercas, troncos, etc.)

L'élevage du renne remonte à des millénaires et se retrouve tout autour du cercle polaire, surtout dans les zones de la planète qui ne conviennent pas à d'autres types d'élevage. Il est surtout le fait de populations indigènes, les Sami en Suède par exemple, et accompagne la biodiversité arctique spécifique ainsi que l'héritage culturel (clôtures, grumes, etc.)

Reindeer farming goes back thousands of years and is found throughout the polar circle, focusing on parts of the world's surface which are unsuitable for other kinds of farming. It is mainly practiced by indigenous people, in Sweden by the Sami people, and is linked with specific arctic biodiversity and cultural heritage (fences, logs etc.).

introduced for transport (planes, off-road vehicles) and communication (radio, GSM). These technological developments are beneficial but require higher farming profits in order to take advantage of them. This translates into needing a herd of at least 400 animals to be profitable. As a result, the number of full-time reindeer farmers is declining.

Right: Due to the decreasing profitability of reindeer farming, the Sami people have been broadening their activities to fishing, hunting and crafts. The latter appears to be a growing market, especially among tourists.
Below: Traditional grazing is threatened by increasing commercial interest (forestry, mining, military activities) and by higher costs due to the modernisation of transport and communication. Over the last decade, the organisation of reindeer husbandry has changed, the farmers forming market corporations and the animal numbers being strictly regulated

Values and Benefits

- **Cultural history**. The tradition of reindeer farming goes back 5,000 years and is integral to the culture of the Sami people. Artefacts, such as very old reindeer pens and traditional stone and log fences, hold tremendous cultural value.
- **Flora and fauna**. The practice of reindeer farming has benefited a number of flora and fauna that rely on the habitat created by grazing reindeer.

Challenges and Threats

- **Grazing rights**. There has been an increase in commercial interest in the northern arctic area for logging, mining, and oil extraction. Although Swedish law protects the Sami's right to graze land, their rightful ownership is often difficult to prove, since they have little written evidence of their past occupation of the land. On the other hand, 'settled' farmers and foresters fear damage by overgrazing, although systems of combined land use have been developed.
- **Deterioration of the natural environment**. Old spruce and pine forests, rich in lichen and other biodiversity, are replaced by fast-growing timber species, resulting in less winter feed for the reindeer. Transport is hindered because lakes no longer freeze due to the building of water power stations and dams. Another well-known example is the 1986 Chernobyl nuclear accident, which contaminated the reindeers' food supply. Consequently, reindeer meat was not allowed on the market for years.
- **Processing regulations**. Since Sweden's accession to the EU in 1995, reindeer slaughtering has had to comply with EU standards. This means additional costs for transport to official abattoirs.
- **Decreasing prices**. Over the last few years, the price for reindeer meat has been dropped by one-third.

Public Policies and Incentives

- **Targeted support**. The EU has co-financed support for investments in reindeer enterprises and the development of reindeer farming and Sami villages. Under the Swedish agri-environment programme, there is specific support for the maintenance of natural and cultural heritage in reindeer farming areas.

Private Initiatives

- **Cultural tourism**. Private markets for tourism and crafts are developing. As the profitability of reindeer farming has declined, many farmers have taken up other activities like fishing, hunting, and crafts. The uniqueness of the Sami culture is attracting an increasing number of tourists, and some Sami are finding ways to capitalize on this interest.

Alaskan Reindeer Farming

Prior to the introduction of reindeer farming to the North American arctic in the late 1800s, Alaskan natives were hunting, gathering, and fishing for survival. But with a dwindling supply of sea game (due partly to fur-seeking white hunters) and wild caribou roaming further inland, it was becoming increasingly difficult to find sustenance. Meanwhile, in another part of the Arctic Circle, the Sami people were taking advantage of reindeer's tendency to munch on lichen, a plant inedible to humans that the reindeer could transform into hearty, abundant meat. Noting the similarities between the Siberian and North American arctic, Dr. Sheldon Jackson, U.S. General Agent of Education in Alaska, decided to introduce the Sami's tradition of farming reindeer to the Seward Peninsula of Alaska.

In the late 1800s, Jackson enlisted the help of Siberian reindeer farmers, and later a number of Norwegian Sami, to teach Alaskan natives how to farm reindeer. The experiment was successful, and eventually, the Alaskan Eskimo population transitioned from a hunting culture to a herding culture, no longer dependent on the whims of the winter sea. Reindeer have remained a vital part of indigenous Alaskan culture, providing transportation, food, and because there are markets for a variety of reindeer products, a means of economic well-being.

One modern example of successful reindeer farming is Nuniwarmiut Reindeer and Seafood Products, a tribally-owned company located on Nunivak Island in Mekoryuk, Alaska. The island has been inhabited by indigenous peoples for over 2,000 years, and reindeer farming has long been part of the area's economy. The company carries on this tradition with the help of various modern innovations, such as the snowmobiles that they use to herd the animals. Another innovation that has aided the reindeer industry is the introduction of a volunteer slaughtering and processing inspection programme that went into effect in late 2003. Prior to the program's instatement, USDA regulations required inspections that made it difficult to distribute fresh reindeer meat locally. When the Alaska Department of Environmental Conservation (DEC) developed state inspections, it gave the Alaskan reindeer industry easier access to inspectors and the opportunity to reach a broader, more profitable market.

Domestic reindeer populations have always fluctuated in response to the problems of predating wolves, overpopulated herds, and the animals' tendency to gravitate towards migrating caribou. But another, much different set of challenges faces the industry today: development, and the resulting habitat change. Increasingly, the mining and hydrocarbon industries are encroaching on land that was previously used for grazing.

Granted, over the years, indigenous peoples of the arctic have developed a myriad of ways to provide for their communities. But reindeer farming remains unique in the reciprocal relationship that it encourages between farms and the surrounding environment. As stated by Norman Chance in a report entitled *The Lost Reindeer of Arctic Alaska*, "Prior to [the introduction of reindeer farming], Eskimo hunting, fishing, and gathering activities basically used nature's renewable resources. But herding reindeer transformed the people's relationship with their natural environment in that Eskimo herders began utilizing it for the production of livestock." Undoubtedly, the loss of reindeer herding would again transform these peoples' relationship with the environment, but not necessarily for the better.

SEMI-ARID LANDSCAPES

Arid and semi-arid landscapes are found on every continent. In some countries and regions like North Africa, Australia, the American West, and central Asia, huge portions of the land receive very low annual rainfall. Humans, plants and animals have adapted to these conditions over millions of years, both through careful conservation practices, like fallowing the land, and ingenious systems of collecting and transporting water, often over long distances.

Both North America and Europe have large semi-arid regions that have supported advanced cultures and civilizations for many thousands of years. These regions also have been home to unique plants and animals, often not found anywhere else on the planet. While large-scale agricultural activities have emerged over the past two decades in some parts of these regions, the climate and limited moisture tends to keep cultivated areas confined to relatively small sized farms and livestock ranches. The large and industrial-style operations that have emerged have attempted to overcome the limited access to water through massive water pumping and irrigation projects. Unfortunately, much of this has come at the expense of other values, such as wildlife conservation and water quality protection.

While there are some negative trends in these regions, there are many positive stories about sustainable, efficient agrarian systems that have survived and slowly evolved over thousands of years amongst the areas' indigenous cultures and people. Alongside these successful traditional approaches are new innovations, like the water-banking concept being used in southwestern North America, that are helping to bring new vitality and resilience to the region.

We begin in Europe, with a look at the *montado* system of agro-silvo-pastoral cultivation found in the dry regions of Portugal and the closely-related *dehesa* landscapes in Spain. These gorgeous areas of evergreen oaks and controlled grazing areas support a wide range of culturally specific farming practices and special biological diversity. We also explore the non-irrigated cereal producing regions of the high plateau regions of central Spain, often called pseudo-steppes.

We then move to North America and explore the Sky Island region that extends from the southwestern US across the border into northern Mexico. Here, large-scale ranches have come together with government agencies and non-governmental organizations to actively pursue environmental restoration and the promotion of biodiversity at the level of an entire ecosystem.

Across Europe and North America

Montados and Dehesas

A primary characteristic of Mediterranean landscapes is their multifunctionality at field, farm and landscape levels. They combine arable crops with forestry and pastoral components. Examples of these landscapes are mountain landscapes with *transhumance*, from Spain to Romania, regularly inundated *lameiros* in Atlantic northeast Portugal, *coltura promiscua* landscapes with former *mezzadria* systems and chestnut-grove landscapes in the sub-Mediterranean hills of France and central and north Italy, as well as montados and dehesas landscapes in the continental plains of southern Portugal and Spain. The following focuses on the latter landscapes.

The Portuguese montado is an agro-silvo-pastoral system, similar to the Spanish dehesa system. The different types of montados cover roughly 1.3 million hectares, and dehesas altogether cover more than two million hectares. Montados and dehesas are characterised by an open oak formation in varying densities (from 40 to 100 trees per hectare), combined with a rotation of cereal-fallow-grazing. The montados and dehesas create a unique panorama and a very specific regional identity charged with many cultural values not found elsewhere in Europe. These qualities attract local recreation and tourism.

Montados and dehesas were formed by the clearing of evergreen oaks from woodlands in areas with nutrient-poor and often shallow, acidic soils that experienced severe moisture deficits in summer months. Cork oaks (Quercus suber) and holm oaks were not cleared and now are the dominant species. Low input cereal crops are grown mainly as supplementary feed for livestock and game. This land use system has existed for several centuries but was optimised in the Alentejo region in the 19th and first half of the 20th century.

Nutrient cycles are maintained primarily by Iberian black pigs, feeding on acorns, shrubs and grasses under the trees. Other grazing species include cattle, sheep and goats. The animals drop their manure, while sheltering under the trees, and loosen the soil, favouring the production of cereals, grasses and trees. Careful tree management (pruning, clearing, thinning, shoot removal) and controlled grazing promote the infiltration of rainwater in the soil. The extensive grazing regime of the Spanish dehesas includes transhumance of large herds over long distances, to and from summer pastures in mountains and on steppes. In this way, problems with low productivity and severe drought in summer can be alleviated. Regular seasonal livestock movements over shorter distances do still occur, as well.

Cork oaks produce wood, originally for charcoal, and cork. These resources are the most valuable product of the montados. Additional products include fruits, honey, mushrooms and aromatic plants. The most productive trees are pruned to remove disease-infested branches, to broaden their canopy and to increase acorn production. Apart from acorns, leaves are used as livestock fodder during dry periods. Shade, vital for the livestock in summer and a contributor to the preservation of soil moisture, ultimately favouring plant production, is another product of the trees.

These landscapes of open stands of oak scrub zones occur predominantly on steeper hillsides, which have been used traditionally for game management. The variations in tree and scrub densities, grazing pressure and rotation with arable cropping create altogether heterogeneous landscapes.

Montados and dehesas can be regarded as European savannas.

Values and Benefits

- **Landscape**. The montado and dehesa landscapes are sometimes called European savannas.
- **Cultural heritage**. The landscape is locally enriched with a network of stone walls, hedgerows, traditional buildings and prehistoric megaliths (menhirs, dolmens, cromlechs).
- **Biodiversity**. Due to the low intensity and the diversity of the land use, the biodiversity of many of these landscapes is high. Many rare and now threatened species are common here, including:
  - **Mammals.** Most indicative of its well-developed animal community is the presence of many large predatory mammals such as the Wolf, the Iberian subspecies of the Pardel Lynx, the Wild Cat, the Genet and the Badger.
  - **Birds.** Large predatory birds and scavengers include the Black Vulture, Imperial Eagle, Bonelli's Eagle, Black Kite, Black-shouldered Kite and the large, nightly hunter — the Eagle Owl. Other birds include wintering European Crane, Black Stork, White Stork, Azure-winged Magpie and the Red-necked Nightjar.
  - **Plants.** In the different types of montados and dehesas, the flora has extremely high diversity per unit area. The flora includes bulb plants such as species of Crocus and Daffodil, including *Narcissus asturiensis, Narcissus bulbocodicum Nivalis* and *Narcissus rupicola* and low shrub species, especially Rosemary, *Cistus ladanifera* and Lavender. Small undershrubs include *Genista triacanthos*, Grace Ward and *Tuberaria lignosa*.

Top: The Black Vulture breeds in oak trees.
Bottom: Azure-winged Magpies in Europe are almost exclusively found in montados and dehesas.

Challenges and Threats

- **Simplification**. In past decades many montado landscapes went through major changes by both intensification and extensification of land use. The result is a simplification of the landscape and severe perturbations of the traditional balance between its components. Often the trees were damaged and eventually died, whereas the natural regeneration was not always taken care of. Extensive areas were abandoned. Subsequently, either a natural succession with scrub encroachment or monospecies plantations of eucalyptus and pines took over, both with increased risk of wildfire.
- **Economics**. In the cork oak montado, the economic viability is still preserved by high cork prices. Commercial cereal production has practically disappeared, but some farmers try to keep the system in balance by growing arable crops and keeping livestock. Livestock production as such is not economically viable unless it is strongly intensified.
- **Degradation**. In the holm oak montado where the cork crop is absent, the main threats are degradation of the tree cover and abandonment of the land. Few farmers have been successful in maintaining the system through specialized livestock production.

Public Policies and Incentives

- **Montados.** There are no policy measures for the landowners of cork oak montados, since cork production is profitable enough. There are four policy measures frequently used by landowners of holm oak montados:

    - **Pasture maintenance**. One measure aims to reduce abandonment of the land through maintenance of natural pastures and shrub control. This measure is mainly applied to shrub clearing. However, this measure alone can be counterproductive if clearings are too radical, damaging the trees and promoting soil erosion.

    - **Grazing support**. Another policy measure supports pig grazing in holm oak montados. Compared to cork oaks, the acorns of holm oaks are sweeter and have more nutrients. This measure helps maintain pig grazing on those farms that still have pigs.

    - **Indigenous livestock**. A third policy measure aims to maintain indigenous livestock breeds. However, where applied in montados, this measure often results in densities that are too great, reducing the natural regeneration of the trees and promoting soil damage by trampling and erosion.

    - **Forage production**. A forth measure is aimed at forage production, and is applicable only to montados with low tree densities.

  In general, these policy measures reduce abandonment of montados. But the unique values of the montado continue to decline, because the measures are targeted at components of the land use system rather than the system as a whole and because the environmental conditions for support payments are not sufficiently integrated into the measures.

- **Dehesas.** Despite the importance of dehesas in Spain, only one regional agri-environment scheme explicitly targets this unique system: the Andalusia Dehesa Conservation Scheme. Under this scheme, farmers receive payments if they deliver environmental benefits according to an approved Integrated Management Plan for their farm. The plan includes management practices with regard to ploughing and tillage, soil erosion prevention, water quality protection, tree conservation, stocking density, preservation of landscape elements, waste and architecture. Additional payments are available for farmers converting land on steep slopes into pastures, pasture restoration, erosion remediation, tree regeneration and public access.

Private Initiatives

- **Landowner commitments**. In the holm oak montados successful private initiatives are limited and completely in the hands of private landowners. Some of these landowners maintain the traditional land-use systems because of cultural and ethical arguments, not because of governmental socio-economic and conservation measures. These landowners value, and feel a responsibility, for maintaining a specific regional identity.

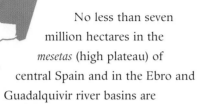

Cereal Steppes in Spain

No less than seven million hectares in the *mesetas* (high plateau) of central Spain and in the Ebro and Guadalquivir river basins are occupied by cereal steppes landscapes. The land use has produced a mosaic of non-irrigated cereal crops, fallow land (long- and short-term), legume crops and dry grasslands. The flat or slightly undulating topography, open spaces and scant vegetation of this system resemble the true steppe landscapes in Russia and Asia, with which it shares some biogeographic features. However, diversity in bird communities, soil type and vegetation, combined with the Mediterranean climate (with average annual rainfall of less than 600-700 millimetres), clearly set the Spanish pseudo-steppes apart.

Human activities (fire, deforestation, grazing and agriculture), most of which date back to the Roman period, have largely determined the present characteristics of these landscapes. However, it is believed that in the more arid zones and in areas with soils unfavourable for vegetation growth (e.g. chalky or salty areas in the depressions) these landscapes would have existed, to some extent, without human intervention. The agro-ecosystem might be classified as a pastured cereal pseudo-steppe. This landscape provides habitat for steppe birds, and attracts birdwatchers from around the world. Areas of extensive cereal production are also important wintering grounds for a wide range of species that breed at more northerly latitudes.

Pseudo-steppe birds are adapted to a dynamic agricultural mosaic. A common rotation on a particular field is one with cereals (wheat, barley and oat), fallow and legumes (luzerne,

vetch) in a three-year cycle. There are huge variations in fallow duration — between one to seven years, depending on soil fertility. Fallow is a traditional technique to cope with the low productivity of farming under limiting farming conditions. During the fallow period soils recover: stubble of previous crops are incorporated into the soil, and livestock dung further enhances its organic matter content. In any case, cereal crop stubble during autumn is typical. Depending on length of fallow, the time available for natural succession also differs, which means that density and composition of weeds colonising the fallow plots are different. Variability of fallow duration between different fields results in spatial and temporal diversification and a heterogeneity of habitat structure, which is positively linked to diversity and abundance of steppe birds. Further, fallow land is itself a habitat particularly selected by most species during the breeding season. After the fallow period, the field is ploughed up and weeds growing there are incorporated into the soil. Traditionally, a leguminous crop is planted, which further enriches the soil with nitrogen. After the leguminous crops, cereals are again planted. In intensified areas there are no leguminous crops planted, and the rotation cycle is reduced to two years.

Agricultural productivity on the pseudo-steppes is quite low, with average cereal production of 2.5 tonnes per hectare, compared to six tonnes per hectare in the European Union as a whole. Extensive livestock husbandry has important functions in this ecosystem, such as the maintenance of short vegetation and soil organic matter and the dispersal of weed species, also consumed by birds. The Merino sheep is economically the most valuable breed, with stocking levels varying between two to three heads per hectare.

Eine Steppe mit Getreidepflanzen und Sträuchern, auf der im frühen Herbst von Cobeña Schafe am Horizont weiden.

Estepa cerealista con arbustos y ovejas pastando al fondo al comienzo del otoño en Cobeña.

Une steppe céréalière, avec ses arbustes et ses moutons en train de paître à l'arrière-plan, au début de l'automne, à Cobeña.

A cereal steppe with shrubs and grazing sheep in the background during early autumn in Cobeña.

Values and Benefits

- **Landscape**. Cereal steppes are characterised by a flat or slightly undulating topography, open spaces and scant tree vegetation.
- **Bird species**. Although not widespread, the main natural values of this agro-ecosystem are the populations of many birds species that are in decline throughout Europe, including the most threatened Hen Harrier, Montagu's Harrier, Lesser Kestrel, Great Bustard, Little Bustard, Stone Curlew, Black-bellied Sandgrouse, Pin-tailed Sandgrouse, Short-toed Lark, Calandra Lark, Crested Lark and Tawny Pipit.
- **Plant diversity**. Low-growing perennial shrubs and higher vegetation like oak and leguminous shrubs are found in abandoned fields, borders between fields and scattered plots.
- **Cultural traditions**. The Merino sheep is a unique race adapted to long-distance transhumance, with the associated environmental and cultural values.

A male Great Bustard showing its nuptial plumage.

Challenges and Threats

The system has experienced a four-way process of change over the last decades:

- **Species loss**. Since before the entry of Spain in the Common Market of the European Community (1986), the agricultural authorities have encouraged intensification of agriculture. Mechanization has intensified, leading to the destruction of bird nests and disturbance resulting in nest abandonment. The repeated ploughing-up of fallows during winter and spring disturb the steppe birds and reduce the weed cover attracting them. With an increased application of fertiliser, the proportion of fallow land is reduced, and legumes have almost disappeared, while cereal stubble continues to be burned in autumn. As a consequence of land consolidation schemes, many hedgerows and shrubs between fields have been removed. Further, irrigation systems are developed where water is available, changing the ecology of the system.
- **Population loss leading to land abandonment**. Lack of profitability and scarcity of young farmers willing to take over farms cause abandonment of agriculture in marginal areas. Rural depopulation is happening rapidly (with densities under 30 inhabitants per square kilometre in some regions), and social functions are not maintained or renewed, driving, in a feedback loop, young people to move out of rural areas. As a consequence, large surfaces of non-irrigated land have been colonised by natural vegetation or have been reforested with fast-growing species, leading to a loss of habitat for steppe birds.
- **Urban development**. In the form of transport infrastructures, power lines, dispersed housing and industrial areas, urban development is taking place in surrounding cities, attracting more people and impacting negatively on the natural values. These developments are usually not perceived as positive by the local people.
- **Minimal financial support**. Financial resources spent on the problems and demands of dryland areas are kept to a minimum, in comparison to those targeting more productive areas, reflecting a low recognition of the unique values of these systems. This lack of recognition frustrates farmers in cereal steppes.

Public Policies and Incentives

- **Programme coordination**. Agri-environmental measures have been developed that are aimed at the conservation of birds in extensive cereal systems, but the financial rewards have been too low for a substantial adoption by farmers. Furthermore, lack of efficient coordination between agricultural and environmental departments results in limited impact due to design deficiencies. However, cross-compliance on direct payments, to be introduced in 2005, is expected to be an opportunity to enhance the environmental performance of agricultural policies. Additionally, specific compensatory allowances for Natura 2000 (the European ecological network) sites, foreseen under future rural development programmes, can encourage the adoption of more nature-friendly agricultural practices in the most valuable areas.

- **Economic diversification**. Other measures have been introduced in the rural development programmes (2000-2006) aimed at income diversification through new activities, tourism and the production of high-quality products. Efforts in the processing and commercialisation of regional products are also financially supported under that programme. Primarily oriented towards raising living standards and population fixation, the impact of these measures on the maintenance of cereal steppe landscapes is uncertain. Technical assistance to farmers and shepherds, provided by environmental authorities, could successfully contribute to the conservation of steppe birds.

- **Formal protection**. Only a small percentage of the cereal steppes have any formal protection. The LIFE-Nature programme of the EU has been applied to co-finance initiatives of environmental and nature conservation non-govenmental organisations (SEO/BirdLife and Adena/WWF) with regard to targeted steppe birds. It is too early to draw conclusions on the impact of these initiatives.

- **Detrimental schemes**. Unfortunately, policy measures with adverse effects are also present. Land consolidation schemes pursuing scale-economy effects from increased field size continue to be structurally supported. Irrigation plans promoted by administrations also threaten the maintenance of cereal steppes and their natural values. Subsidies for reforestation of agricultural land have had similar severe negative impacts for the steppe habitats.

- **Decoupling**. Recent reform of the EU Common Agricultural Policy (CAP), introducing payments decoupled from production could result in ambiguous effects, further marginalisation and abandonment in some areas and intensification through the introduction of more profitable non-cereal crops in other areas. Some of the threats could be reduced with integrated agriculture and environmental policies and policies for land planning. Specific conservation measures should be designed, monitored and adapted continuously to reach their conservation aim.

Interview with Juan de Mesa

Juan de Mesa is a 54-year old dryland farmer in Cobeña, a small village 30 kilometres north of Madrid. (Pictured at right with his daughter Jimena.) Juan inherited from his father both the pride of being a farmer and the natural curiosity and respect towards the Great Bustards inhabiting his fields. He owns 100 hectares and rents twice that, with an average field size of two hectares. He considers himself a lucky farmer, since this farm-size, together with good markets for his eggs, makes his farm economically viable.

What conservation actions do you implement on your farm?

"I went into the extensification measure of agri-environmental schemes when these began in 1996, although the payments hardly compensate for the loss of income derived from the compulsory one-hectare set aside. However, I learned as a child helping my father that the harvesting combine could destroy the nests of the Great Bustard and other birds lying in the ground, lost in the wheat. I always have the combine operator take precautionary measures: If I am aware of where the nest is, I have the operator leave a one-metre patch around the nest in order to disturb the nestlings as little as possible. Since I do not always know the precise location of nests, and want to give adult birds and chicks the opportunity to escape, I ask the operator to begin harvesting from the periphery of each field, moving forward concentrically to the centre, and to put a hanging-chains device in front of the combine. In this way birds have the opportunity to escape well in advance, avoiding bird-killings otherwise common. Other precautions include taking extra care when ploughing and chemical-spraying. I always try to leave a half-meter wide unploughed edge with my neighbours' fields and avoid spraying these strips. This is not only beneficial for beetles, butterflies and other insects, but also for rabbits, who find refuge in this vegetation."

How do you see the future of your farming and your farm?

"Well, I have heard that CAP aids are evolving towards more environmental concerns, but the precise determinations for the next campaign are not yet known. However, seeing as this production begins to have a market, I am considering entering into organic farming schemes. I face this stage with uncertainty since things are changing rapidly. For example, the village is expanding, and a couple of my fields could soon become building land soon. Given the offered prices, I would have no options…."

Southwestern United States & Northern Mexico

One of the most hauntingly beautiful landscapes of North America is the vast desert region that straddles the border between the southwestern United States and the northern states of Mexico. For thousands of years, the people and the land have been in a gentle balance, supporting some of the most advanced indigenous cultures on the continent and dotting the high country with pueblos and small villages. The unique ecosystems in this arid and semi-arid region of the southwestern US provide special habitats for rare and endangered plants and animals.

Throughout this region are unique mountain ranges — often called Sky Islands. Each of these mountain 'islands', thanks to the last major glaciation, have developed separately from one another, evolving unique geological, biological, and topographic features that create unique habitats. It is a phenomenon similar to what happens on oceanic islands, where plants and animals evolve in isolation. The 40 mountain ranges that make up the Sky Islands can be imagined as a terrestrial archipelago. These Sky Islands have remarkably moderate climates in the midst of harsh deserts. Some of these forested mountains rise over 3,000 metres and provide dramatic ranges of climate.

Indigenous people have been farming this land for thousands of years, and European settlers have been ranching here for over 300 years. Land ownership patterns have remained intact for very long periods of time, which has resulted in the land being held in very large-scale sections: some of the area's ranches cover hundreds of square kilometres. Keeping the land in these ecosystem-sized units has provided wide-open spaces for wildlife and has reduced the possibility of extensive commercial development that would increase pressure on limited water supplies. As a result, this agrarian landscape has help preserve some of the most unique flora and fauna in North America. In these mountains bears and parrots live together. Jaguars, mountain lions, and wolves are free to roam over the great distances they need to flourish, including the deserts in between.

In recent years, however, there has been increased economic pressure on landowners due to falling market prices for their livestock, timber and other products. Fearing that these pressures could lead to the breaking up of these large ranches into sub-divisions for recreational development and second homes, a number of the local residents began to meet together to talk about ways to protect and preserve the agrarian nature of the landscape.

These private discussions became public in 1992, when the US Forest Service made a proposal to turn the Coronado National Forest in southeastern Arizona into a National Recreation Area — a plan that could have led to devastating effects on the land and the people of the region. This brought into the public arena a series of debates that had been taking place in private over the future direction for the region.

Out of these meetings a new public organization was created, called the Sky Island Alliance, to bring together environmentalists, public officials, landowners, ranchers and other concerned citizens to create the conditions for the restoration of the full range of native species and ecological processes in the region. As a result of their work over the years, more than 200 individuals and dozens of organizations, community groups, and government

agencies in the United States and Mexico have worked to develop a comprehensive, overarching conservation plan for the Sky Islands Wildlands Network, released in the fall of 2000. This massive Sky Island Wildlands Network Conservation Plan calls for the proper balancing of actions that would "maximize protected parks, wilderness areas, and roadless regions" while at the same time providing strong support for ecologically-minded land uses such as ranching.

The public policies needed to develop this broad vision draw upon the resources of all levels of government and the private landowners. The 'midwife' role of conservation and environmental organizations has been crucial, along with the biologists and ecologists who have brought the scientific expertise needed to create a well-grounded vision for the whole region.

A good example of this collaboration being fostered by the Alliance is the effort to build 20,000 gabions, or small dams, on the El Coronado Ranch. These small, dry-stacked stonewalls are used to slow the flow of water down the tiny creeks that dot the countryside. In a region that gets only a half meter of annual precipitation, it takes conscious planning and an enormous amount of work to find all the ways to help conserve moisture and to turn this into sustenance for plants and animals, both wildlife and livestock.

Die 40 Bergketten, aus denen die Sky Islands bestehen, kann man sich wie eine Inselgruppe auf dem Land vorstellen. Rancher und Umweltschützer arbeiten gemeinsam, um die einzigartige Artenvielfalt dieser Region zu schützen.

Las 40 cadenas montañosas que conforman la región de Sky Islands pueden describirse como un archipiélago terrestre. Los rancheros y los expertos en medio ambiente cooperan para proteger la biodiversidad única de esta región.

Les 40 chaînes de montagne qui constituent les îles Sky, c'est presque comme un archipel terrestre. Les éleveurs et les écologistes travaillent ensemble à la protection d'une biodiversité unique dans cette région.

The 40 mountain ranges that make up the Sky Islands can be imagined as a terrestrial archipelago. Ranchers and environmentalists work together to protect the unique biodiversity of this region.

The Diablo Trust

In Coconino County, Arizona, two enormous ranches sit side by side. The Prosser and the Metzger families have been neighbors for more than eighty years. Their combined ranches, the Bar T Bar and the Flying M, consist of nearly 200,000 hectares of federal, state, and private lands spread across a broad swath of northern Arizona, between Mormon Lake and the town of Winslow, in the center of the Sky Islands region. This massive holding covers six different biological zones that range from ponderosa pine forest at 2,300 metres in elevation to Little Colorado River valley desert scrubland at 1,500 metres. It is home to a diverse wildlife population, including four threatened and endangered species.

The agrarian landscapes created by these two massive tracts of land are crucial to the breeding and propagation of a number of rare and endangered plants and animals. A unique feature of these ranches is that because of their size, they encompass, and protect, ecosystem-sized habitats.

The two families who own and operate these ranches understand the importance of preserving this land as intact, working landscapes and the need to build community support to ensure this over the long-term. To build stronger links with the local communities, they created the Diablo Trust with the stated mission of "maintaining ranches as long-term, economically viable enterprises managed in harmony with the natural environment and the broader community." Besides the two main ranching families, this Trust includes environmental activists, government range and wildlife officials, artists, academics and students, recreation enthusiasts and hunters, and local residents. "The collaboration allows us to work within a community, and the community to work with us," explains Jack Metzger, one of the original founders.

Work with the community has thus far included research projects by scientists from Northern Arizona University and Prescott College on comparative grazing practices, riparian and wetlands areas, piñon-juniper regeneration and distribution, as well as various wildlife studies. Besides providing scientific feedback for future decision-making, these projects involve students and community members as hands-on participants. The scientific community has come to appreciate the knowledge and know-how of those who live and work on the land.

The Trust is also conscious of the cultural aspects of their mission. During annual 'Artists on the Land' days, visual and performing artists, writers, and musicians are invited to enjoy the beauty of the ranchland and to create songs, poems, and pictures in celebration. The results are then displayed and performed at the 'Reflections of the Land' Art Show at the nearby university

In recognition of these unique collaborations, Diablo Trust has been designated a National Reinventing Government Laboratory and honored by the federal Environmental Protection Agency. A key accomplishment cited has been the restoration of a nearly two thousand hectares of watershed through removal of invasive juniper trees. This has allowed native grasses to re-establish themselves and has produced a richer, more diverse plant community — thereby benefiting both cattle and wildlife.

Values and Benefits

- **Habitat preservation**. The land ownership patterns created by the Sky Island region's ranching system keeps large-scale habitats intact, providing many rare and endangered plants and animals, like jaguars and parrots, the large areas needed for breeding and propagation. As a result of these special conditions, this area is home to more than 2,000 different plant species, 265 species of birds — including 30 sub-tropicals — 90 mammals, and nearly 190 different snails. The 75 reptiles that are found in this region represent the most diverse herpetological region in the United States.

- **Water conservation**. Thanks to their unique climates, the mountains in this region have many perennial streams, allowing for the evolution of a high number of endemic species. Ranching provides the economic basis for maintaining the conservation practices needed to protect these water sources.

Challenges and Threats

- **Competing interests**. Along with its incredible biological richness, the beauty and power in this landscape attracts visitors from all over the planet, often creating conflicting land use demands. Sacred Indian ceremonies, camping, hunting, rock climbing, military training exercises and logging are part of the mix of human activities competing for space and water in this fragile zone.
- **Urban development**. Land sales and transfers threaten long-term, sustainability-minded agreements and relationships, leading to uncertainty and disruption of ecosystem-level planning and management. The sale of large-scale land units for sub-division into parcels for second-homes now threatens rare habitats.
- **Detrimental policies**. Federal and state government agencies' policies and practices are increasingly hostile to conservation programs and policies. For example, the recent North American Free Trade Agreement has led to a decline in prices for some key agricultural products from semi-arid regions, causing increased pressure on owners to liquidate holdings.

Century plants are succulents native to the Southwest's grasslands and have traditionally been used by Native Americans in the region.

Public Policies and Incentives

- **Laws**. Federal laws like The Endangered Species Act have been used to successfully protect habitat, and subsequently, farmland.
- **Coordinated planning**. Coordinated ecosystem-based land management planning by local, state and federal government agencies is encouraging resilience for fragile regions.

Private Initiatives

- **Marketing**. Product branding and labelling programs have proven effective, providing consumers with channels for supporting wildlife friendly ranching in this region through the marketplace. Marketing campaigns are being used to boost consumer awareness and interest in agricultural products from local producers in this region.
- **Rural tourism**. Carefully planned tourism options are being developed to help local landowners to both diversify their business revenue streams and to boost overall income, thereby reducing some of the economic pressure to sub-divide or inappropriately develop large-scale holdings.

Mediterranean Landscapes

Mediterranean climates are found in Europe, North Africa, the southern coast of Australia, coastal South Africa, and in the US state of California. These areas are alike in their dry, hot summers and cool, wet winters. This mix of desert-like and cool-wet weather has created unusual biodiversity. Many plants, for example, go dormant in the hot rainless summers and then come back to life when the rains begin again in the fall and winter. The Mediterranean climate zone tends to coincide with the biome or vegetation zone commonly called the scrub forest, or chaparral in North America. In this region you can often find smallish, drought-resistant shrub and tree species.

The different Mediterranean zones that grace our planet are relatively small and distant from one another. Together they make up less than two per cent of the Earth's terrestrial area. While these regions are famous for their wines, and all share important food crops such as wheat and olives, each has a rich and distinctive biodiversity with an impressive number of native fauna and flora, many endangered.

For thousands of years the cultivation of food and fibre crops in what is now Europe's Mediterranean region provided the underpinnings for the growth of great civilizations. Even today, alongside the massive expansion of tourism and other industries and service economy companies, small scale, ecologically specific farming remains crucial to the protection of this landscape.

This chapter looks at olive production in Europe, one of the oldest and most enduring crops produced in the region. Olive production, especially in its traditional form, provides valuable employment opportunities within Europe, as well as refuge for disappearing species. Thus, preservation of olive groves is not only an environmental issue, but a social one as well.

From North America, we look at an example on the central California coast, where relatively small farmers near the major cities of San Francisco, Oakland and San Jose have developed a unique approach to farming and to preserving their fragile landscape.

European Olive Groves

The olive tree, *Olea europaea*, has been cultivated for more than 40 centuries for its edible fruit and valuable oil. The subtropical evergreen tree is native to the eastern Mediterranean region where it may have been originally cultivated by Semitic people several millennia ago. Though wild olive trees still grow throughout southern Europe and northern Africa, their domesticated counterparts are more common, varying from secondary derivatives to highly productive cultivars.

As the trees require two to three months of cool temperatures in order to produce flowers and fruit, their growth is restricted to certain climate zones. The trees can grow well on different soil types, but have some preference for calcareous soils and a partiality for the sea breeze. The trees grow very slowly, but can grow very old and wide — trees up to 700 years old and trunks with 10 to 15 metres in diameter have been recorded. Planting practices include spacing trees a standard distance apart (an olivette) to guarantee a balance between undisturbed growth and production.

Within Europe, the five main olive producers are Spain, Italy, Greece, Portugal and France. According to EU estimates, there are currently about 750 million potentially productive olive trees, a cumulative acreage of five million hectares.

There are three main types of olive plantations:

- Traditional plantations with scattered trees, that require little or no inputs of water, fertiliser and pesticides, but require high inputs of labour.
- Intensified traditional plantations, with a higher tree density, that require more fertiliser and pesticides and intensified soil cultivation.
- Intensive modern plantations that use smaller trees, planted in high densities, and make systematic use of modern mechanisation, fertiliser, pesticides and irrigation.

Im Mittelmeerraum gibt es 5 Millionen Hektar Olivenhaine mit traditionellen Plantagen, was Künstler wie Van Gogh inspiriert hat. Andererseits gibt es auch moderne Plantagen mit üblicherweise vollkommen maschinell betriebener Bearbeitung, Düngung und Spritzung sowie manchmal, wie im südspanischen Andalusien, mit Bewässerungssystemen.

En la zona mediterránea existen 5 millones de hectáreas de olivares. Esta cifra incluye tanto explotaciones tradicionales que han inspirado a artistas como Van Gogh, como plantaciones modernas en las que se hace un uso intensivo de medios mecánicos, fertilizantes y de la fumigación, y en ocasiones del riego, como en Andalucía.

Dans la zone méditerranéenne, nous trouvons 5 millions d'hectares d'oliveraies. Ils comprennent les plantations traditionnelles, sources d'inspiration pour des artistes comme Van Gogh. Il y a en outre les plantations modernes, souvent fortement mécanisées, fertilisées et traitées, parfois irriguées, comme en Andalousie en Espagne.

In the Mediterranean area, we find 5 million hectares of olive groves. These include traditional plantations, which have inspired artists like Van Gogh. On the other hand, there are modern plantations that are usually heavily mechanised, fertilised and sprayed, and sometimes irrigated, like in Spanish Andalucia.

The plantations vary considerably in productivity: from less than 500 kilograms per hectare per year for traditional plantations to over 10,000 kilograms per hectare per year for modern irrigated ones.

Although olive production now stretches as far as Argentina, California and Australia, the five European countries are still the biggest producers, dominating 80 per cent of the world's olive oil market. The farming of olives provides employment for a large number of people in rural areas, including 2.8 million registered producers in the European Union. Many of these are small or part-time olive farmers: the number of large-scale commercial olive farms is relatively low.

The environmental effects of olive farming are cause for heated controversy. The more intensive plantations are particularly detrimental to the natural environment. They produce a monotonous landscape and rely heavily on pesticides, fertilisers and irrigation, depleting biodiversity and irreversibly altering the composition of the land. In contrast, the more traditional plantations can be very beneficial:

Values and Benefits

- **Scenery and landscape**. The older, uniquely shaped trees have tremendous aesthetic and cultural value. They have inspired artists such as Van Gogh, and in the Homeric world were a symbol of luxury and wealth.
- **Plant diversity**. Where undergrowth consists of natural vegetation, it can boast a diversity of wildflowers, insects and butterflies that support a variety of bird species.
- **Bird diversity**. Birds like Little Owl, Scops Owl and Hoopoe breed in the gnarled trunks of old olive trees. Other species, like the Quail and the Partridge, breed and forage in the vegetation surrounding the base of the tree. A third group, including the Woodlark and Stone Curlew, nests between the trees on semi-open ground. Unfortunately, in some regions, birds are considered a nuisance because they harm the fruit and are systematically killed.
- **Stone walls**. Terraced plantings are usually separated by dry stone walls, providing habitat for herbs, insects and reptiles.
- **Genetic diversity**. As there are numerous olive varieties and olive trees can grow very old, traditional olive groves play an important role in maintaining genetic diversity. In Italy alone, nearly 300 varieties have been listed, but only few of them are grown in large numbers. Currently, there are very few initiatives in place to preserve genetic diversity in olive farming.

Landschaftlich betrachtet sind die traditionellen Olivenhaine am wertvollsten, aber auch am bedrohtesten. Der Wiedehopf brütet in den alten Baumstämmen, und der Boden kann viele Pflanzen- und Insektenarten beherbergen.

Desde el punto de vista paisajístico, los olivares tradicionales son los más valiosos, pero también los más amenazados. La abubilla se alimenta en los viejos troncos y la maleza puede ser rica en plantas e insectos.

D'un point de vue paysager, les oliveraies traditionnelles sont les plus intéressantes. Mais ce sont aussi les plus menacées. La huppe fasciée se reproduit dans les vieux troncs et la couverture végétale est riche en espèces végétales et en insectes.

From a landscape perspective, the traditional olive groves are the most valuable, but also the most threatened. The Hoopoe breeds in the old trunks and the undergrowth can be rich in plant and insect species.

Challenges and Threats

Over the last two decades, olive farmers have faced an unfavourable economic situation:

- **Limited profit**. Olive prices have gone down due to overproduction, partly resulting from EU schemes. This price decrease is especially harmful to small producers with traditional, low-yielding plantations.
- **Pests**. Diseases, fungi and insects such as the olive-fly have seriously affected yields.
- **Production-oriented support**. Government support favours production-oriented farms over traditional farms. As a result of the huge differences in yield per hectare, support levels vary from less than € 100 per hectare in traditional groves to over € 2,000 per hectare in modern plantations.
- **Abandonment**. Due to this unfavourable situation, the number of abandoned or neglected olive plantations is increasing, especially among the plantations that contribute most to landscape beauty and biodiversity.

Public Policies and Incentives

- **Equalizing support**. The protection of olive groves is contingent upon policy within the European Union and critical changes will be required for traditional groves to receive the same level of protection and support that modern plantations receive. Policy measures within Europe to support the production and protection of olive trees rests on the demand for olive oil. European support for olive oil originated in 1966 when Italy was the only olive oil exporting country. Until recently, the majority of EU subsidies were production-based, thus enticing growers to intensify production and replace old groves with new plantations. Nearly the entire budget of the EU's olive regime (around € 2.5 billion) has been spent on subsidies rewarding the most productive and profitable olive farms. In 2001, support was granted for 2.1 million tonnes of olive oil, of which Spain produced 50 per cent.
- **Values-driven supports**. The new EU proposals for the olive regime are less production-oriented. Forty per cent of the budget will be spent on an Olive Grove Payment to favour olive groves of environmental and social value. The remaining 60 per cent will be included in the single farm payment and become a fixed payment, no longer rewarding intensification. This payment, however, will be based on subsidies received in the past, thus still favouring intensive farms over extensive ones. Environmental non-governmental organizations have been proposing a flat-rate area payment instead.
- **Need for broader support**. Although all olive growing countries have been implementing agri-environment schemes, olive groves have rarely been included up until now. It is estimated that only about five per cent of the total EU olive acreage will be able to benefit from such a scheme (e.g. for maintenance of habitats or stone walls).

Italian Olive Farmer, Roberto Soragnese

Mr. Roberto Soragnese runs an eight hectare organic olive farm in Bovino, in the Italian Puglia region. He produces 100 tonnes of olives or 20-25 tonnes of olive oil. The farm contains old trees, placed irregularly throughout the grove. Weed control takes place mechanically.

"The grove is rich in biodiversity and contains wild trees and shrubs like hawthorn, bramble and wild rose, and small rodents, reptiles and passerines," Mr. Soragnese explains. "However, the production is under severe pressure due to low prices, lack of consumer awareness and failing EU support policies. In a traditional grove like mine, the labour costs are about twice the price we receive. In addition, in order to sell my organic oil, not mixed with oil of other producers, I have to invest in an oil mill, in bottling and in marketing."

Mr. Sorangnese continues,

"Consumer awareness is still very low: the majority just buys the cheapest oil, regardless of its origin and its environmental effects. In this region, there is no agri-environment scheme to award our efforts. Moreover, the EU support policy favours big farms producing at lower cost but with less quality and more environmental damage. There will only be a future for our farm if policies and consumers focus on food quality and environmental benefits."

Die traditionellen Olivenbauern befinden sich in einer ungünstigen sozioökonomischen Position: Nach der Überproduktion sind die Preise gefallen, und die Politik der EU-Subventionen hat kaum hochproduktive Agrarbetriebe unterstützt. Somit wird eine ständig wachsende Anzahl an wertvollen traditionellen Olivenplantagen nicht mehr bewirtschaftet oder ganz aufgegeben.

Los olivareros tradicionales se encuentran en una posición socioeconómica desfavorable: la sobreproducción ha provocado la caída de los precios y el régimen de ayudas de la UE ha estado beneficiando solamente a las explotaciones más productivas. Cada vez existen más valiosos olivares tradicionales descuidados o abandonados.

Les agriculteurs traditionnels qui cultivent l'olivier se trouvent dans une position socio-économique difficile: suite à la surproduction, les prix ont chuté et le régime d'aide de l'Union européenne favorise surtout les exploitations à grosse production. Un nombre de plus en plus important de plantations traditionnelles intéressantes sont négligées ou abandonnées.

Traditional olive farmers are in an unfavourable socio-economic position: as a result of overproduction, prices have gone down, and the EU support regime has been merely favouring highly productive farms. An increasing number of valuable traditional plantations are being neglected or abandoned.

California's Central Coast

One of the largest Mediterranean regions in the world lies on the western coast of North America, mostly within the state of California. This area has attracted millions of immigrants from the Mediterranean regions of Europe due to the similarity of the regions' climate and landscape. Over the past three centuries, this landscape has welcomed wave after wave of new immigrants but has retained much of its original character. This region is still considered one of the most beautiful in all of North America.

The richness of the plant and animal resources in the region has been abundant enough to sustain steady population growth until very recently. Intensive agriculture was introduced in the early 19th century as Spaniards migrated to California. The Gold Rush of 1849 brought new people and ideas to the area, including the introduction of modern farming practices and the division of the landscape into large-scale farms. In the 1850s and 1860s, dairy farming, fruit and vegetable production, and oyster culturing were introduced, creating products destined for the growing nearby city of San Francisco. At the same time, immigrants began pouring into the region from Italy, Portugal, Greece and the Azores, bringing additional crops and advanced farming techniques.

Marin County, near San Francisco, exemplifies the classic Californian mediterranean landscape, with rolling hills, coastal bluffs and flat interior valleys separated by hills that are dotted with chaparral and oak woodland communities. Soil quality varies and water supplies are unpredictable, making the region poorly suited to intensive agriculture. Along the coast, however, foggy, moist conditions keep the grasses on the hillside green throughout much of the year. These rich grasslands have supported herds of dairy and beef cattle for over a century. For the past 125 years, milk and dairy products have dominated the county's farm sector (currently accounting for 65 per cent of the $50 million (US) annual total agricultural sales), with livestock production, particularly beef cattle, generating the second largest share of farm income. The rich alluvial soils in the valleys support diverse vegetable and specialty crops, and an increasing number of small operations are producing organic vegetables for California restaurants and farmers' markets. This small but growing niche currently generates over $800,000 (US) in annual sales.

Farmland occupies 50 per cent of Marin County, or approximately 67,600 hectares. Of the county's nearly 300 farms, 74 per cent are considered small or mini-farms, with an annual gross income of less than $100,000 (US). The rich history of farming in Marin County is illustrated by the fact that a majority of farms here are third- or fourth-generation, family-owned operations. Some of the dairy farms in this region have been producing high-quality milk since the 1800s. In 1913, local milk producers established the California Cooperative Creamery to process and distribute their milk, butter and cheese. Today most Marin County milk is still processed at the creamery in the city of Petaluma before going to market. About 20 per cent of the region's milk comes from Marin dairies.

In the 20th century, the entire West Coast region — from

Marin County mit seinen sanften Hügeln, Steilküsten und durch Hügel getrennten flachen Tälern, die mit Waldbeständen und Eichenwäldern übersäht sind, ist ein Beispiel für die klassisch mediterrane Landschaft Kaliforniens.

Marin County constituye un ejemplo de paisaje californiano mediterráneo clásico, con ondulantes colinas, acantilados costeros y valles interiores separados por colinas, salpicados de bosquecillos de chaparrales y robles.

Le Marin County est un exemple classique du paysage méditerranéen californien, avec ses collines arrondies, ses falaises et ses vallées intérieures plates séparées par des collines et parsemées de chaparral et de quelques chênes regroupés.

Marin County exemplifies the classic Californian Mediterranean landscape, with rolling hills, coastal bluffs and flat interior valleys separated by hills, dotted with chaparral and oak woodland communities.

British Columbia in Canada to the Baja Peninsula in Mexico — experienced rapid growth in population. In Marin County, the population increased from just fewer than 16,000 people in 1900 to some 85,000 in 1950 and then more than doubled by 1970. In these latter decades, rural areas located near major cities were developed for housing and industry at dizzying rates of speed. Between 1949 and 1982 about 317,000 hectares, or roughly one-quarter of the San Francisco Bay area's farmland was lost. Since 1959, Marin County alone has lost 13,000 hectares of agricultural land, and the total number of ranches has declined from 1,800 in 1944 to less than 300 today. In just over two decades, from 1950 to 1972, the number of dairy ranches in the county was cut in half from 200 to 100. To make matters worse, the early 1970s saw the development of major highway plans that, if realized, would have devastated Marin agriculture.

Fortunately, county residents took action to prevent further irreversible losses of farm and natural areas. Particularly important in the effort to save Marin County farms was a group of farmers, ranchers and environmentalists who came together in 1980 to create the Marin Agricultural Land Trust (MALT), the first organization of its kind in the US. The organization was created to lobby local and state officials and, ultimately, the national government to enact laws and policies that would stop development from replacing farming in the West, particularly in the beautiful and biologically rich coastal areas of Marin and surrounding counties. MALT has achieved phenomenal success, protecting 13,350 hectares of farmland from development with agricultural conservation easements: contracts between the landowner and another entity — often the local or federal government — that limit the right of the landowner and subsequent owners in the kinds of activities that are allowed on the land. The main goal of these easements is to ensure that the land remains in farming.

The past three decades have also seen the establishment of public Open Space Districts and private land trusts in all of the major agricultural districts surrounding San Francisco, including Marin's northern neighbour, Sonoma County, where voters have approved a modest increase in the local sales tax to fund conservation easements. The success of these innovative public and private partnerships in protecting important landscapes has inspired groups throughout the US to develop similar initiatives.

Values and Benefits

- **Open space**. Liveability in this population-dense region is dramatically enhanced by the close proximity to the open countryside provided by the regions farms.
- **Habitat**. Farmland provides habitat for many species, including rare and endangered plant and animal species.
- **Fresh, local food**. The farmland in the region provides residents of the Central Coast access to fresh, high quality food grown locally.

Challenges and Threats

- **Development**. Despite some successes, real estate developers are working to reverse legislation and policy that currently protect some of the most richly biodiverse farmland in this region.
- **Economic pressures**. Low market prices for agricultural products continue to threaten many producers' long-term economic sustainability.
- **Cuts in research budgets**. Reductions in public investments in agricultural research have created a widening gap between the needs of producers and the availability of tested innovations in crops and techniques.

Public Policies and Incentives

- **Purchasing policies**. Public institutions, especially schools and hospitals, are beginning to adopt purchasing policies that favour locally and sustainably-produced foods, thus dramatically expanding the size of the market for the region's producers.
- **Conservation schemes**. New legislation could be enacted to prevent the weakening or undermining of existing conservation schemes and enhance the protection of sensitive areas through permanent easements.

Private Initiatives

- **Green initiatives**. Landowners and urban dwellers are working together to protect land from commercial development through conservation easements and other green initiatives.
- **Local markets**. Consumers in nearby cities have become more aware of the value of preserving prime farmland and have come together in cooperative ventures to create market opportunities for local, sustainably-grown agricultural products through producer-to-consumer links.
- **Institutional markets**. Private hospitals are choosing to support local farmers by re-directing their purchasing to favour products coming from the nearby countryside.

ISLAND LANDSCAPES

Islands are a special kind of agrarian landscape, often remote and small-scale. Our planet has hundreds of thousands of them, including hundreds of island regions and dozens of island states. Indonesia, for example, consists of more than 17,000 islands, while the Philippines has more than 7,000. The largest island in the world is Greenland, covering over two million square kilometres. The Australian continent is the second largest. While some islands, like Manhattan, New York, are completely urbanised, the majority are scarcely populated or not inhabited at all.

In order to be eligible for targeted support, islands in the European Union must meet certain size and population criteria. This distinction sharply limits the number of 'recognised' islands. Greece, for example, has over 3,000 islands, but only 129 of them meet the EU criteria. Before the recent expansion, the European Union contained 286 'recognised' islands, covering 3.4 per cent (100,000 square kilometres) of the total territory and providing home to more than 13.5 million islanders, about 3.5 per cent of the total population. In Greece and Italy, however, the share of islanders is over ten per cent.

While the island state of Hawaii is by far the most well known island in the US, there are significant islands in most states, as well as thousands scattered throughout the Great Lakes and off all seacoasts. The Aleutians, the San Juan Islands off the coast of Washington State, Puerto Rico, and the US Virgin Islands in the Caribbean, Cape Cod and the Barrier Islands off the coasts of Florida, Georgia, South and North Carolina are just a few of the many islands that have developed significant year-round and seasonal populations.

There are many significant challenges facing island dwellers today, but they are not necessarily insurmountable. After all, the first industrial revolution took place on the island of Great Britain, and the Japanese archipelago is home to one of the world's leading economies. Most islands, however, lag behind. In the EU, for example, income of most islanders is less than three-quarters of the EU average.

Many islands face a serious handicap: they are mountainous or part of an archipelago. These geographic quirks require complicated transport networks and increased investment in infrastructure. Because the mainland usually offers the largest markets, islanders face even more transportation expenses. Sometimes the remoteness of islands is relative: the Greek island of Rhodes lies 560 kilometres from Athens, but only 20 kilometres from Turkey, with which it has (for historical and political reasons) very little trade. In the US, islands like Hawaii and Guam are even further offshore.

In this chapter, we present examples of island farming in Greece (the Aegean Islands), the Netherlands (the Wadden island of Terschelling), and from the Hawaiian Islands in the United States.

Santorin ist eine der 3000 griechischen Inseln im Kykladen-Archipel. Die terrassenartige Landschaft ist typisch für viele der gebirgigen griechischen Inseln. Die Entfernung der Insel vom Festland (75 km) verursacht beträchtliche zusätzliche Transportkosten.

Santorini, que forma parte del archipiélago de las Cícladas, es una de las 3.000 islas griegas. Su paisaje en terrazas es típico de la mayoría de las islas montañosas de Grecia. La distancia que la separa de tierra firme (75 km) supone un coste sustancial adicional para el transporte.

Santorini est l'une des 3.000 îles grecques ; elle fait partie de l'archipel des Cyclades. Le paysage en terrasse est typique de bien des îles montagneuses grecques. Son éloignement du continent (75 km) entraîne des frais supplémentaires substantiels en matière de transport.

Santorini is one of Greece's 3,000 islands, part of the Cyclades archipelago. The terraced shaped landscape is typical for many of the mountainous Greek islands. Its remoteness (75 km) from the mainland creates substantial additional costs for transport.

The Greek Aegean Islands

The Aegean Sea is an arm of the Mediterranean Sea, located between the Greek peninsula and Anatolia, which is now part of Turkey. The Aegean was the birthplace of several ancient civilisations, including the Minoans of Crete and the Cycladic, Ionian and Mycenaean Civilisation of the Peloponnese. The islands in the Aegean Sea can be divided into seven groups. Both of the islands examined in this section — Naxos and Santorini — are part of the Cyclades, a ring of 220 islands around the sacred

island of Delos. Aside from two volcanic islands, the islands are peaks of a submerged mountainous terrain, and, except for Naxos, the islands are not very fertile.

As is the case in the rest of Greece, farms on islands usually specialise in either animal husbandry or cropping (rotational or permanent). Animals are kept extensively, mainly on public land. Livestock farming is dominated by goats and sheep, while cattle and pig farming are much less common. Cropland is usually fragmented in small parcels, with an average farm size of about three hectares. Traditionally, farmers on the islands have grown a wide variety of crops, including cereals, legumes, vegetables, grapes and olives.

The hilliness of the islands requires farmers to use terracing techniques, which originated in prehistoric times. All of the aforementioned characteristics — fragmentation, multicultivation and terracing — are common to virtually all islands. Yet climatic and microclimatic conditions differ greatly among islands, ensuring that every island is unique. For example, precipitation on the Greek Islands ranges from 400 to 1,100 millimetres annually.

On Naxos (right), cereal terrace cropping became less profitable than the mechanised cropping used on the mainland. As a result, many of these terraces have been abandoned, and their contributions to biodiversity and scenic beauty lost

Values and Benefits

- **Landscape**. The Greek islands offer a spectacular combination of terraced mountains, white houses, volcanic remains and seaside vistas. A distinct landscape feature of some islands is the presence of narrow stone-covered paths that connect fields with villages, windmills and watermills, and small stone buildings used for storage.

- **Flora**. The islands are a treasure of flora, fauna and diverse habitats. Habitat types vary among and within the islands according to the landform and climate. Olive groves, vineyards, fields, orchards and pastures are often rich in wild flora, including rare and endemic species such as the Red Tulip in the fields of Chios. Many olive groves are rich in orchid species as well.

- **Fauna**. The islands' farmland is home to many animals, both vertebrates and invertebrates. Amphibians find refuge in man-made small stone water reservoirs. Turtles, lizards and snakes — some rare, some endemic — are found on farmland, where they forage and hide from predators. For the same reasons, a number of rodents (rabbits, porcupines and weasels) inhabit agricultural land. On the island of Samos, a remarkable species, the Jackal, lives on and near farmland. Also, large numbers of birds, some of them rare or endangered, depend on farming and farmland. On Crete, for instance, the Bearded Vulture depends on animal husbandry, feeding on carcasses. The same holds true for the Griffon Vulture on Naxos. On Lemnos, the rare Lesser Kestrel is associated with farmland.

Island farming offers spectacular landscapes and a rich biodiversity with many endemic species. On the island of Naxos, for instance, the Griffon vulture is related to farmland.

Challenges and Threats

- **Abandonment**. The unique and picturesque landscapes of the Greek islands are threatened by land abandonment and major changes in land use. Abandonment tends to occur in stages, beginning with the abandonment of certain crops (cereals, legumes, most of the vegetables) due to low productivity (often related to lack of water) and a high cost of production. The second stage is the ceasing of all agricultural activities, including the neglect and degradation of terraces. Finally, the population of an island may decline. Some of the smallest have already been left without farmland habitats. Fortunately, over recent years there has been a reverse trend on some of the islands.
- **Reduced diversity**. Each stage of abandonment reduces the diversity and aesthetic value of the landscape, along with the quality of farmland habitat and biodiversity.
- **Better paying work**. The Aegean islands have become very popular with tourists. While tourism is an economic opportunity for islanders, including those who farm, it can also draw people away from farming because of its attractive revenues.

Public Policies and Incentives

- **Targeted government action**. To address island-specific problems, Greece created a separate Ministry of the Aegean in 1985.
- **Island specific provisions**. The EU has put in place a number of provisions specific to islands in regards to farm policy, taxation and customs:
  - more flexible rules on state aid, especially for the Aegean islands and other remote regions.
  - higher ceilings on special government funding for regional development and socio-economic cohesion.
  - tax and customs exemptions. The Greek tax system provides tax reductions for legal persons and associations undertaking activities on small islands with less than 3,100 inhabitants.
- **General policies**. The islands also benefit from more general policy measures:
  - Ninety-eight per cent of the island population is eligible for assistance under the EU funds for regions that are lagging behind and for improvements in transportation and energy networks.
  - Agri-environment schemes. Large parts of the islands qualify for these programmes. Recently, a grant scheme for the restoration and maintenance of terraces was introduced.
  - Special regional programmes to support innovative rural development and regional cooperation.
- **National investments**. Extensive national investments are being made in sea and air transport, infrastructure, island industries (including farming and fisheries), access to public services and the development of 'green tourism' and 'green energy'.

The Naxos Integrated Environmental Management Project

At 428 square kilometres, Naxos is the largest and most fertile of the Cyclades islands. Agricultural products of the island include wine, fruits, wheat, olives and tobacco. Cereal cropping, once an important activity, has become less profitable compared to the mechanised cropping of cereals on the mainland. Despite substantial revenues from mining and tourism, the island is considered one of the least developed Greek islands in terms of economy, family income and development. Furthermore, it faces an increasingly ageing population.

In the mountainous village of Aperathos, an important sustainable development experiment was launched in 1992, under the enthusiastic guidance of Mr. Manolis Glezos, the former mayor of Aperathos. The project was co-financed by the EU. The village population had been decreasing rapidly, falling from 2,500 to 1,000 inhabitants, with a significant number of families still trying to make a living from livestock rearing and other farming activities. The experiment began as an effort to tackle local water shortage problems but was expanded to address a wide range of water and soil-related problems such as:

- the reduction, and sometimes extinction, of native vegetation.
- soil degradation and exposure of bedrock due to severe erosion problems.
- abandonment and destruction of cultivated terraces. The terraces, some of them nearly 5,000 years old, had functioned as water reservoirs that reduced run-off and erosion.
- the lowering of water tables and exhaustion of water reserves due to intensified water supply.
- salination, the intrusion of sea water into coastal plains.

The innovative experiment was integrated into the community, relying on village authorities, local organisations, and the substantial involvement of local residents to achieve success. The project was also an excellent example of the use and integration of advanced scientific knowledge and technologies into traditional local practices.

The project combined the twin objectives of expanding and regenerating local agricultural activities and the restoration of hill and mountainsides. The day-to-day work was carried out by 156 workers from Aperathos and three neighbouring villages, many of whom were educated 'on the job'. As a result of the project, the water infrastructure has been restored and renewed, the slope vegetation has been reestablished, and many cultivation terraces have been fixed or rebuilt. The latter, combined with the provision of irrigation water, has motivated the Aperathos inhabitants to redevelop agricultural activities.

Santorini: the SantoWines private initiative

Santorini, or Thira by its ancient name, is a small circular group of volcanic islands 75 kilometres southeast of the Greek mainland. It has a surface area of 80 square kilometres and a population of 10,700. Santorini is the most active volcanic centre in the Aegean Arc and boasts the world's largest caldera. Its volcanic lava burned and fractured the surrounding rocks, making the soil absorbent, porous, and rich in porcelain — perfect for growing wine grapes. The 'trapped humidity' of the

mountains combined with the morning dew create a particular micro-climate in which the grapes can survive the islands' long hot summers. Winemaking in the Cyclades islands goes back more than 3,500 years. There are currently 850 growers who cultivate 2,500 hectares of vineyards (about one-third of the island). Because Santorini has no rivers, water is provided from small springs and frequently has to be imported.

In addition to wine, the island produces cherry tomatoes, capers, barley, pistachios, watermelon and goat milk, in addition to vegetables like white eggplant, peas, beans and potatoes. There are also two plant varieties endemic to Santorini: the fava bean and a local cucumber variety called *katsounia*.

SantoWines is the Association of Cooperatives of Theraic Products, founded in 1947 to protect the financial interests of the Santorini farmers. All of the island's farmers are members. The main activities of the cooperative are the production, processing and marketing of wine and tomatoes (the island's most important products) and the management of fertilisers, pesticides, forages and farm equipment. The cooperative buys all farm products, to ensure that farmers receive sufficient income to keep farming, and tries to find adequate markets for them. In this way, the revenues of the most successful island wines compensate for weaker markets for other products.

Since the 1990s, SantoWines has been modernising its production and distribution. In addition to building a new winery and Wine Promotion Centre, the cooperative has expanded its marketing to the Greek mainland and to France, Germany, Canada and the United States. A key to their success in expanding the export market has been the willingness on the part of cooperative members to increase the transparency of their production processes in order to demonstrate their compliance with the highest safety standards.

Terschelling, a Dutch Wadden Island

Terschelling is one of six islands north of the Netherlands, separated from the mainland by the Wadden Sea, a large North Sea estuary famous for its birds and seals. It is a long, thin island with an area of 9,000 hectares and 4,700 inhabitants. The 1,000-hectare agricultural region is situated on the south side of the island, along a series of dykes that hold back the waters.

The 40 farms on the island are all livestock farms, with nearly half in dairy operations and four specialised sheep farms. The livestock density is relatively low: 80 per cent of the dairy farms have less than one cow per hectare. Island farms face added costs of transporting to and from the island all the farms' needs and products. For instance, farmers must have their fertiliser, feed, cattle, and building materials shuttled to them by boat. For an average Terschelling farm, these transportation costs total about 15,000 — about 15 per cent above the regular production costs of a product that already has very narrow economic margins. Many farmers try to compensate for these additional production costs with supplementary income from tourism, conservation measures and the sale of regional products. The island's popularity among tourists helps substantially.

Terschelling is also rich in biodiversity. In winter, the island shelters thousands of geese, including a significant proportion of the world population of Brent geese. In spring, the island is host to numerous ground-nesting birds, some of which breed on farmland. Over the years, programmes have been created to compensate farmers for allowing the geese to forage on their grassland and for taking care of ground-nesting birds by actively protecting the nests. Thanks to the widespread adoption of these agri-environment schemes on the island, populations of Black-tailed Godwit and Redshank are increasing.

Auf der niederländischen Insel Terschelling gibt es eine harmonische Koexistenz von Natur und Landwirtschaft.

La isla holandesa de Terschelling constituye un ejemplo de coexistencia armónica entre naturaleza y agricultura.

L'île néerlandaise de Terschelling, exemple d'une coexistance harmonieuse entre nature et agriculture.

The Dutch island of Terschelling showing a harmonious coexistence of nature and agriculture.

Interview with Egbert Zorgdrager

Dairy farmer Egbert Zorgdrager operates a 100-hectare grassland farm that produces 650,000 kilograms of milk. He is the chairman of the island's farmers' cooperative for nature conservation. The Netherlands currently has over 100 such local initiatives where farmers work together for the benefit of nature conservation and economic diversification.

"I started farming here with my father in 1987 and took over the farm in 1993, converting the dairy farm to an organic one, as did two other farmers on the island. Our milk is processed into Gouda cheese in a small dairy factory on the island. This factory was a small-scale private initiative, started in 1993. The cheese is sold on the island to local residents and tourists, but mainly in health stores in the densely populated western part of the country. We receive six Eurocents more per kilogram for our milk over our non-organic colleagues, but we have to cope with higher costs for land, organic feeds and lower production per cow. However, in this way we can — to a certain extent — convert the 'natural handicaps' of the island into conservation and tourism opportunities and, as a result, island farming can be viable in the future."

"The government agri-environment incentives are very important, but the private markets for organic cheese and green tourism also substantially contribute to our farm incomes and compensate for the relative cost disadvantage of farming on an island. And it suits me well, as it is not feasible to farm here like in parts of the mainland. It enables me to get paid for the time I put into conservation measures in the interest of geese and grassland birds. The farmers' cooperative tries to motivate farmers on the island and uses agri-environment schemes as effectively as possible. Nowadays, about 90 per cent of the land and farmers participate in the compensation scheme for accepting geese, and about two-third of landowners participate in measures for protecting nesting birds and field margins. An important opportunity for farmers who are not afraid to give up some privacy is the popularity of the island with tourists. An increasing number of farmers have been starting to sell their products off-farm and to run bed-and-breakfasts, camping facilities or farm tours."

Right: In winter and early spring, Terschelling attracts a large population of Brent geese. Many farmers try to compensate for the added, island-specific production costs with additional income from tourism, conservation measures and sales of regional products like Wadden cheese.

The Hawaiian Islands

Most images of North America highlight its vast prairies, plains and forests, but there are also numerous biologically and historically priceless landscapes throughout the continent's islands. In their multifunctional roles as agricultural producers, stop-off points for seagoing cargo and tourism magnets, the islands encapsulate the challenges facing a variety of regions.

The Hawaiian Islands, off the west coast of California in the Pacific Ocean, are by far the largest and most well know islands. Hawaii is a string of 137 distinct islands encompassing a land area of 16,633 square kilometres. It is the most isolated island chain in the world and home to the most northern coral reefs on the planet. The Islands encompass a wide range of climates and terrain. Annual precipitation ranges from 20 centimetres on some islands to over 1,000 centimetres on others. Elevation stretches from sea level to 4,267 metres. And almost all of the planet's variation in soil is represented throughout the islands' terrain.

Although Hawaii accounts for less than one per cent of total US land area, 75 per cent of US biological extinctions have occurred on the island chain. Hawaii is home to more than one-third of the birds and plants on the US endangered species list, and nearly 60 per cent of its total native flora and fauna is threatened or endangered — the highest percentage of any state in America.

With only 1.5 million people, Hawaii is one of the smallest states in the United States in terms of population, but it is an economic powerhouse. Unbroken landscapes of farmland have been part of Hawaii's history for over 150 years. Today, however, huge parcels of prime farmland are being developed at a rapid pace for housing and tourism. The rising land values that have resulted from this commercial development make it difficult for many farms to survive as agricultural enterprises.

Despite many challenges, agriculture remains the state's third largest industry, with over $500 million (US) each year in sales of primary crops including sugar, pineapples, flowers, nuts, cattle, coffee, milk, eggs and other specialty food products. While agriculture is a big player in the state's economy, it is more highly valued as a key ingredient in the Hawaiian struggle to 'stay green' and to protect the thousands of unique plant and animal species that have evolved as a result of being isolated by the oceans. In fact, lobbying to keep sugarcane production profitable through federal US farm legislation has come from the Hawaiian congressional delegation, who understands that losing the profitable sugar industry would lead to the immediate subdivision of much of the most beautiful and biologically irreplaceable parts of the main islands for housing and resorts.

In addition to federal legislation to keep Hawaiian cane sugar producers profitable, there have been a number of local, state and federal laws passed to help preserve and protect Hawaii's landscape. Back in 1978, Hawaii revised its State Constitution to add a special section that stated, "The State shall conserve and protect agricultural lands, promote diversified agriculture, increase agricultural self sufficiency and ensure the availability of agriculturally suitable lands."

Native Hawaiians are a key force in protecting farmland and a richly diverse landscape. Native Hawaiian culture is often strongly aligned with environmental conservation priorities in

Taro is an important root crop grown on wetlands in Hawaii.

regards to both terrestrial and marine resources. The Hawaii State Constitution, the highest law on the islands aside from the US Federal Constitution, ensures that Native Hawaiians can access land to gather plants for traditional cultural and medicinal practices. Interestingly, the largest private landowner in the state is a trust that holds nearly 150,000 hectares of land on five islands for the benefit of Native Hawaiian children.

In recent years there have been renewed efforts to preserve the cultivation and cultural aspects of important native crops, such as the cultivation of the root crop commonly called taro (or poi when cooked). Taro is a perennial herb, primarily grown in wetlands or constructed water-filled terraces. New programmes are being implemented which connect Hawaiian youth to their history and cultural heritage by involving them in taro cultivation and cooking.

Finally, recent events have influenced Hawaii's commitment to its agrarian landscapes. With the temporary disruption in air and sea transportation resulting from September 11th, residents have grown increasingly concerned about the state's food insecurity. From diversifying crops to turning towards non-traditional agricultural industries, public debate is bringing the issue of agricultural preservation on the Islands to the forefront.

Andrew Hashimoto, Dean of the College of Tropical Agriculture and Human Resources at the University of Hawaii, summarizes the situation in this way, "Knowing that our food supply lanes can be disrupted and that bio-terrorism may be an increasing threat, we must act now to ensure that we have an adequate, dependable, safe food supply for our citizens."

This interest in food security, is just another element that is encouraging a small trend towards returning to a more balanced and diversified agriculture. During the economic recession of the late 1990s, Hawaii's only growing industry was diversified agriculture, although growth was still very small,about one per cent annually. Nonetheless, Hawaii is the only state in the United States where the number of farms is slowly but steadily increasing and the average age of farmers is declining.

Values and Benefits

- **Conservation**. The agriculture landscapes of Hawaii are crucial for preserving and purifying the water and for preserving habitat for many plant and animal species.

- **Preserving green space**. Agriculture slows urban sprawl, and therefore helps keep the landscape green.

- **Food security**. Local agriculture provides Hawaiians with food security, which is of special concern on an island where weather and security problems could disrupt transportation to and from the islands.

Ungebrochene Agrarlandschaften sind seit über 150 Jahren ein Teil der Geschichte Hawais. Die ständige Wertsteigerung des Landes als Ergebnis der kommerziellen Entwicklung macht heute jedoch vielen Landwirtschaften das Überleben schwer.

Los horizontes ininterrumpidos de terreno agrícola han formado parte de la historia de Hawaii desde hace más de 150 años. En la actualidad, el valor creciente del suelo debido al desarrollo comercial dificulta la supervivencia de muchas explotaciones.

Des paysages ininterrompus de terres agricoles font partie de l'histoire d'Hawaï depuis plus de 150 ans. Aujourd'hui, l'augmentation des prix des terrains, due au développement économique, rend la survie des exploitations agricoles difficile.

Unbroken landscapes of farmland have been part of Hawaii's history for over 150 years. Today, rising land values resulting from commercial development make it difficult for many farms to survive.

Challenges and Threats

- **Declining prices**. Declining world prices for tropical products, including sugar and tropical fruits, are forcing landowners to accept offers to develop their farms into hotels, housing and retail shopping malls.

- **Urbanisation**. Rare and endangered plants and animals are facing increasing pressure from urban and tourism developments, creating multiple challenges for land use planners and conservation biologists.

- **Invasive species**. When invasive species enter the state, often through trade and tourism, they threaten endemic flora and fauna.

- **Unstable climate**. Climate change and fluctuation translate into extreme weather events and temperature changes on the islands.

Public Policies and Incentives

- **Conservation policies**. Strong policies to protect biological diversity of all kinds, plants, animals, soil types, etc., can help mitigate some aspects of development pressure.

- **International commodity agreements**. Agreements, like OPEC, can be developed to stabilize prices for commodity producers. Stable price levels make it possible for landowners to keep highly productive land in cultivation and out of real estate development.

Private Initiatives

- **Local markets**. A small but significant number of young farmers are leading the way towards increased diversification of farming and crops. Island supermarkets are now carrying between 30 to 40 per cent fresh produce from in-state farmers, a significant increase over the last decade.

- **Specialty markets**. Medicinal herb production for mainland markets has created important income opportunities for smaller producers.

- **Planning**. Sustainability discussions within the tourism industry are bringing attention to the need for more conscious land use.

LARGE-SCALE CEREAL LANDSCAPES

One of the most characteristic and widespread agrarian landscapes is provided by cereal production. More than half of the world's food energy comes from a limited number of varieties of three 'mega-crops': wheat, rice, and maize. Worldwide, over 700 million hectares of land are used for cereal production, of which 40 per cent lies in Asia, 25 per cent in Europe and the former Soviet Union, and 15 per cent in North America. World cereal production totals two billion tonnes, including 580 million tonnes of wheat, 900 million of coarse grains (feedstuff) and almost 600 million tonnes of rice.

Wheat is the most widely grown cereal grain, covering 17 per cent of the earth's cultivated farmland. It is the staple food for one-third of the world's population, providing more calories and dietary protein than any other crop. Urbanisation in Asia has caused changes in eating patterns, leading to a shift from rice to wheat and thus increasing wheat's relative importance worldwide.

In 2001/2002 the EU produced 208 million tonnes of cereals on 36.3 million hectares. Small-scale cereal production is common throughout most of Europe, while large-scale cereal cropping is practiced in countries like France, the United Kingdom and in some parts of Central and Eastern Europe. With the collapse of the collective systems in Central and Eastern Europe, production in this part of Europe seriously declined, but it has been increasing again since the late 1990s. Cereal farming on an even larger scale can be found outside of the EU in countries like Ukraine and Russia.

In the United States, the lion's share of the available cropland has been devoted to corn, soybeans, wheat, barley, and other oilseeds and small grains for much of the last fifty years. The evolution of this into a form of rotating monocultures, with a huge section of the land devoted to only one or two crops over many years, has created a number of economic, ecological and social conditions that are now showing up as important challenges for local communities and policymakers.

In this chapter, we present examples of large scale cereal farming from the Île-de-France region around Paris, France and from the 'cornbelt' of the United States.

Île-de-France

France grows nine million hectares of cereal crops. While the cereal area is more or less stable, the area used for oilseed crops and other protein crops has increased tenfold over recent decades, totalling 2.5 million hectares in 2003. France is also the largest producer of rape (colza) in Europe, with 1.1 million hectares devoted to this use.

The Île-de-France region surrounds Paris, a major metropolis with much economic activity. Of the 11 million French, 20 per cent live on two per cent of the French territory. Long ago, in the Tertiary Era, four plateaus were formed in this part of the country, each with a calcareous character. More than half of this highly urbanised area is currently in agricultural use, creating wide horizons interrupted only by farms, solitary trees, and small forests.

Most of the 583,000 hectares of agricultural land in the Île-de-France is arable, and two-thirds of it is planted in cereals. In recent decades, the number of farms has dropped, mostly due to urbanisation. Between 1988 and 2000 alone, the number of farms decreased by one-third. Farm scale has been increasing accordingly: in 2000, 40 per cent of the farms were over 100 hectares. Set-aside land includes about 39,000 hectares.

There are four Regional Parks in the Île-de-France, and all have fully integrated the conservation of the plains (including landscape elements like solitary trees, woodlands and small wetlands) into their objectives. The parks are Haute Vallée de Chevreuse (1985; 24,300 hectares), Vexin Français (1995; 65,000 hectares), Gâtinais Français (1999; 63,600 hectares), and Oise-Pays de France (2004; an inter-regional park of 60,000 hectares). The parks are partly meant to serve as a barrier against urbanisation, but they also encourage farmers to take care of the aesthetic and ecological features of their landscape. In 1994, the so-called Green Plan for the Île-de-France introduced a 'green belt' of 300,000 hectares between 10 and 30 kilometres from the Parisian Notre-Dame church. Its purpose is mainly recreational: to provide hikers, cyclists and riders with a mix of attractive landscapes.

Der Anbau von Getreide in der Region der Île-de-France ist wegen der Ausdehnung des Stadtraums, der hohen Landpreise und Produktionskosten sowie der abnehmenden EU-Subventionen einem sehr starken Druck ausgesetzt. Langfristig gesehen werden sogar Großbetriebe nicht in der Lage sein, mit anderen Produktionsregionen mithalten zu können.

El cultivo del cereal tradicional de la región francesa de la Île-de-France está gravemente amenazado por la expansión urbanística, los elevados precios del terreno y los costes de producción, además de la reducción de las ayudas de la UE. A largo plazo, puede que hasta las explotaciones a gran escala no puedan competir con otras regiones productivas.

La culture céréalière dans la région de l'Île-de-France subit la forte pression de l'expansion urbaine, du prix élevé des terrains et des coûts de production ainsi que de la diminution de l'aide de l'UE. À long terme, les grosses exploitations peuvent elles aussi se trouver aux prises à des difficultés et ne plus pouvoir rivaliser avec d'autres régions de production.

Cereal farming in the Île-de-France region is under severe pressure due to urban expansion, high land prices and production costs, and decreasing EU support. In the long run, even the large-scale farms may not be able to compete with other production regions.

Values and Benefits

- **Landscape**. To some people, the large scale and monotony of the landscape may look mundane. But many others, including the inhabitants of the Île de France region, truly appreciate this majestic landscape of wide horizons, immense skies, and yellow waving corn and rapeseed (colza). This landscape certainly contributes to the diversity of European landscapes.
- **Biodiversity**. Although the plant and animal species connected to large-scale cereal farming have been declining due to an increasing use of fertiliser and pesticides and a shift from spring sowing to winter sowing, the cereal plains still support substantial biodiversity. What the Grouse is for the UK uplands, the Grey Partridge is for this landscape. After a sharp decline in partridge populations, due to the use of insecticides and irrigation, several conservation projects have successfully drawn attention to the factors affecting the recruitment of young birds, thus helping to increase nesting densities. Other biodiversity elements include birds like the Montagu's Harrier, mammals like Brown Hare and Mice, and plant species like Red Poppy, Corn Flower and Shepherds Needle. Over time, however, these species have literally been marginalised. On fallow and set-aside land, biodiversity can be much higher than on cultivated cropland, though this depends on whether there is no cover, green cover, or special seed mixtures that attract insects and birds.

Large-scale cereal farming offers majestic horizons and — although it is under pressure — some biodiversity including nesting Montagu's Harrier (left) and species like Red Poppy and Corn Flower (above). Wild plant species are more and more restricted to field margins.

Challenges and Threats

- **Urbanisation**. The farmed landscape, including its aesthetic and biodiversity values, is under severe urban pressure. In 50 years, 100,000 hectares of fertile land has been lost to the expansion of Paris, representing a rate of 2,000 hectares lost every year. The pressure of urbanisation has also led to relatively high land prices, which increases production costs. As a result, the number of farms dropped by two-third between 1970 and 2000. In an effort to find an environmental balance between the city and the countryside, the Paris Urban Development Plan (1994) has restricted the use of agricultural and natural land for development purposes.

- **Price cuts**. In 1980 the EU became a net exporter of cereals, thus creating economic and trade problems. Surpluses were dumped on the world market with export subsidies. As these led to budget problems and criticism from trading partners, the EU reformed its grain policy in the early 1990s. Further price cuts were partially compensated for by hectare payments, so-called decoupled support. In addition, larger farms were required to set aside part of their land. Further price cuts followed under the EU's Agenda 2000 reform. Overall, the price support for grains has been cut by nearly 45 per cent in the last ten years. This has seriously affected the viability of cereal farmers in the region. Despite the relatively large scale of these farms, they appear to be unable to compete with the much larger scale (and lower land prices) found in other specialised cereal cropping regions in the world.

Public Policies and Incentives

- **From price to farm support**. The French institute for agricultural research (INRA) has calculated that the French cereal sector will be hit hard by the above-mentioned Common Agricultural Policy reform measures, especially specialised cereal areas like Île-de-France. It is expected that the decoupled support will not be sufficient to keep the area economically viable. However, the alternative of higher prices and more land set-aside is not likely to be seen as acceptable under current WTO agreements.

- **Agri-environment schemes**. The French version of this EU scheme includes measures for arable fields and field margins. While the latter are quite popular among smaller-scale arable farms in, for instance, the United Kingdom and Germany, participation in the Île-de-France region has been very limited, as the farmers do not perceive the measures as fitting their farms well.

Private Initiatives

- **Tourism**. Farmers could enhance their incomes by offering services (food and drinks, bed-and-breakfast) and 'right of path' to tourists. In the densely populated Paris suburbs this might be a promising initiative, though only for a limited number of farms.

- **Marketing local foods**. Regional Park labels have been developed and efforts are made to increase the processing and marketing of branded mint and water cress (Gâtinais Français), a rabbit-based speciality (Le Lapin Compôte), apple juice (Vexin Français), yoghurt and goat cheese (Haute Vallée de Chevreuse).

The Blue Earth River Basin

The majority of the agrarian landscape in the United States is devoted to the growing of feed and food grains, oilseeds, and other cereal crops. Ideal soils and climate have made it possible to develop highly productive farms of small and moderate-size that have supported millions of farm families and the surrounding communities. It is this landscape that sustains much of the rural culture and society for North America. This is especially true in the midsection of the United States, often know as the cornbelt. In this multi-state region, which includes Ohio, Indiana, Illinois, Iowa, Minnesota and Nebraska, corn and soybeans are the predominant crops, covering a majority of the farmland.

Twenty years ago, while the landscape looked similar from a distance, a closer look told a different story. In the 1980s, while the land was covered with similar crops, its ownership was much different. Then many families farmed relatively small sections of land. In addition to their corn and soybeans, they often diversified their income with small-scale livestock production and other crops. Today, many farms have gone out of business and a much smaller number of farmers are farming much larger acreages. This has resulted in an intensification of agriculture. Even with the best equipment, farming large acreages can mean compromising conservation efforts.

In parts of the cornbelt, efforts are underway to help small and mid-sized farms remain in business. The benefits include maintaining rural populations to keep small towns and cities vibrant and the belief that farmers with more manageable acreages can be more attentive stewards of the land. Furthermore, the increased financial risks of agriculture coupled with a demand by consumers for local foods is encouraging more diversification. While corn and soybean crops are critical to the region's economy, many farmers are reducing their financial risk by diversifying their operations. Interest in fresh, local foods and in health and food security are helping to drive this trend.

Finding a long-term sustainable solution to family income is crucial to the survival of rural community and culture in the United States. The families on the land in this region have few options other than income from the productive and profitable use of working landscapes. There are many important initiatives underway to help preserve family farmers and the rural communities that they sustain in order to protect basic values and cultural aspects of North American society.

The Mississippi River, the largest and longest in North America, is in the heart of this region. As the third largest river in the world, the Mississippi is the convergence of millions of creeks, streams and river systems that drain nearly two-thirds of the arable land and about 40 per cent of the total continental United States. One of the largest of these tributaries, the Blue Earth River, drains much of the southwestern region of the state of Minnesota, right in the heart of the Upper Midwest region.

The Blue Earth region was shaped by massive glacial flows 12,000 years ago, when glacial Lake Minnesota deposited millions of tonnes of soil and debris in this area in very gentle, nearly flat

Der großflächige Anbau von Getreide und Sojabohnen beherrscht das Landschaftsbild im Mittleren Westen der Vereinigten Staaten. Es werden bereits viele Anstrengungen unternommen, um kleinere Farmer dazu zu ermuntern, ihr Land weiterhin zu bewirtschaften, um den wichtigen Schutz und kulturellen Nutzen aufrecht zu halten.

El cultivo del maíz y la soja a gran escala domina el paisaje del medio oeste estadounidense. Se está intentando animar a pequeños agricultores a que permanezcan en estas tierras con el fin de preservar importantes ventajas culturales y de conservación.

Dans la région du Middle-West américain, ce sont surtout les cultures intensives de maïs et de soja qui dominent le paysage. On encourage aujourd'hui les plus petits agriculteurs à rester sur leurs terres afin de renforcer la protection de la nature et de préserver les retombées culturelles.

Large scale corn and soybean farming dominates the landscape in the midwestern portion of the United States. Efforts are underway to encourage small-scale farmers to stay on the land to preserve important conservation and cultural benefits.

landscapes. One-third of the land has less than two per cent slope, and three-fourths has less than six per cent. Thanks to the glaciers, this region has some of the most valuable and productive farmland on the planet.

The 2.2 million acres of land that make up the Blue Earth Basin are situated in the heart of southern Minnesota and northern Iowa's large-scale row crop agricultural region. Accordingly, these lands are planted from 'fencerow to fencerow' with corn and soybeans, covering 93 per cent of the land. Most of these crops feed intensive livestock and poultry operations in the region and supply raw materials to the growing number of regional ethanol and biodiesel refineries. While some crops are still exported to foreign countries, the increasing use of genetically modified varieties in the region has hurt export opportunities. Consumers in the EU and Japan have made it clear that this will likely remain a problem for US farmers.

The technology and techniques of agro-industrial farming systems are in wide use in this highly fertile region, resulting in phenomenal corn and soybean yields. These same techniques, however, cause problems for the environment, the farmers and their rural communities. One of the major problems is that this area contributes significantly to the pollution load in the Mississippi River. Ironically, the very soils that create the high yields also play a role in worsening this problem. A fine clay soil type, called loam, dominates the region. Once suspended in water after a heavy rain, these clay soil particles stay suspended until the water stops flowing. Phosphorous often attaches to the clay when the soil erodes. This soil also allows for ready 'leakage' of nitrogen, which is applied heavily in the production of corn crops here.

The role of the soil in facilitating the run-off of sediment, nutrients, and pathogens is exacerbated by the huge and intricate man-made drainage infrastructure that has been built to drain the regions' wetlands and other low-lying areas. This system has become a 'freeway' that quickly transports pollutants to nearby surface waters, from which they eventually flow down the Mississippi to New Orleans before out to the sea. Nutrient run-off from fields and factory-style animal feedlots throughout the Midwest has become a primary contributor to the gigantic 'dead zone' in the Gulf of Mexico.

Periodic flooding has always occurred in these rivers and interconnected water systems and, in fact, is necessary for the health of the ecosystem: many aquatic plants thrive on periodic submergence and exposure. However, flood mitigation efforts, channelisation of rivers, siltation, and a host of other alterations have degraded wetlands and backwaters into sterile, silt-laden basins that no longer provide habitat to wildlife.

Values and Benefits

- **Tall grass prairie landscape**. This region houses some of the last surviving remnants of the continent's original tall grass prairie.
- **Wildlife habitat**. Within the Basin are a wide range of habitats, including hillside forest, floodplain forest (wooded bottomlands), wooded bluffs, oak savanna (a rare and endangered habitat), wet meadows, emergent marshes, fens, grasslands, sand prairie, and the open water of lakes, streams, and creeks. These habitats support a wide variety of birds, mammals (deer, fox, and beaver), and over thirty species of frogs and reptiles, including snakes, and turtles. Bald Eagles have recently recovered from near extinction — to the point that they have begun building nests in the tall trees along the riverbanks. Other species abound, as well.
- **Flyway**. About 40 per cent of all North American waterfowl use the Mississippi River as a migratory flyway. Thirty-five per cent of the continent's bird species (326 species) travel along this corridor in their spring and fall migrations. Like other wildlife, the birds find many hospitable habitats in the Basin.
- **Communities**. Many rural communities are sustained by this agrarian landscape, forming the basis for much of the rural culture and society in North America.

Challenges and threats

- **Decreasing farm revenues**. Persistently low farm gate prices for the main crops of corn (maize) and soya have pushed many small and medium-sized producers out of business, causing major depopulation problems in the region. Farmers still on the land often feel forced to farm more and more intensively to make up in yield and overall volume for the low prices.
- **Farm and trade policies**. Federal farm policies and international trade policies also favour increasing intensification of production by supporting commodity pricing schemes.
- **Lack of public awareness**. Many people do not know about the biological, ecological, economic, and cultural importance of prairie landscapes. This creates a barrier to developing a level of public concern about the degradation of the Basin that might result in financial support for reconstruction and re-orientation of land use.

Public policies and incentives

- **Price stabilization**. Programmes are needed to ensure above cost of production market prices for all of the major crops.
- **Habitat protection**. One major effort to intervene in the face of trends causing loss of wildlife habitat was the creation of a protected area called the Minnesota Valley National Wildlife Refuge. Within the boundaries of the park, the vast array of habitats described above are preserved. Government scientists and technical staff all manage and protect these habitats through biological control of pests, prescribed burning to kill off unwanted sapling trees, water control structures, invasive plant removal, integrated pest management, seeding, planting, encouraging natural regeneration, and working cooperatively with neighbouring cities, land management agencies, and nature organizations. While important, this set-aside only encompasses roughly ten per cent of the land area in the Basin.
- **Conservation incentives**. The Conservation Security Program (CSP) and other policies provide incentives for farmers to shift into landscape conservation and environmental protection activities and away from intensive cultivation. These programs focus on the 90 per cent of the Basin lands that are or have been in agricultural production. A major public-private partnership in this region, the Blue Earth River Basin Initiative (BERBI), has successfully worked to bring significant amounts of public and private funding into the region to help farmers shift to producing alternative crops and more value-adding activities.
- **Best management practices**. Federal government funding for large-scale implementation of 'best management practices' on farmland, coupled with tightening regulations for water quality, has accelerated the deintensification of farming in the region. BERBI is a great model of a successful collaboration between government agencies, non-governmental organisations, and grassroots farming organisations, and their effectiveness was a major factor in the USDA's decision to use the Basin as a test site for the CSP when it was first developed as a way to reward corn and soybean farmers who adopted more sustainable practices.
- **Local government efforts**. Many local government entities in the region are working to mitigate the negative impacts of federal agricultural policies in areas of primary concern, like threats to drinking water quality and negative impacts on tourism.

Private initiatives

- **Landscape-based recreation**. Many landowners in the Basin are actively pursuing alternative land uses such as recreational hunting and bird watching that have the potential to increase their revenues even as they de-intensify production (which, in turn, helps the wildlife populations on which these activities depend).
- **Marketing local foods**. Local, sustainably-grown food products are being promoted in nearby metropolitan areas, helping to improve the economic situation of producers who are working to preserve the landscape and support their own communities by maintaining local ownership of the land and patronizing local processors and distributors.

Interview with Tony Thompson

Tony Thompson's family has farmed in southwestern Minnesota for many generations. Conservation-minded and deeply committed to protecting the agrarian landscape and way of life, their Willow Lake Farm has been nurtured to be one of the most ecologically sound and biologically diverse farms in the entire nation.

Today, Tony farms over 650 hectares of corn and soybeans. He uses a tillage system where seeds are planted on permanent ridges in the soil. This system helps the soil absorb water, rather than having it run off into ditches, streams and wetlands. "We've learned that there's less than one quarter of runoff water coming from the ridge till fields compared to those tilled conventionally," Tony explains. "When the water finally does come, it's much cleaner — there's much less soil and attached herbicides and fertilizers in the runoff water." Tony is also experimenting with planting red clover, annual rye grass, and other crops among his corn and soybeans in order to improve soil ecology.

Tony's interest in ecology has led him to preserve parts of his land in tall grass prairie and woodlands. "I remember taking a botany course when I was 21 and the only flowers I knew then in southwestern Minnesota were the Pasque Flower, the Blue Flag Iris and maybe the Violet," he says. "Today I can identity over 200 species of plants that live on or near my farm."

Tony has turned his interest in prairies into a profitable business. "About 15 years ago I started to make an attempt to combine the seeds [from the prairie]. Now I've got a huge seed crop. This last year we got thousands of pounds of

seeds." Tony uses an old combine to harvest seeds in August and October. He then sells the seed crop to the Minnesota and Iowa Departments of Natural Resources. Tony is glad to have an economic reason to be protecting the prairie but is even more delighted to have provided a haven for birds like the Sandpiper, as well as a multitude of prairie plants and mammals like deer, fox and raccoons.

Tony now hosts an annual Agro-Ecology Summit on his farm as a way to explore and promote the work of all of his neighbors who are farming with nature. This event also helps to educate policymakers and other opinion-leaders about the importance of protecting agrarian landscapes, but making sure they are economically, socially, and environmentally sustainable.

MIGRATORY LIVESTOCK PRODUCTION: *TRANSHUMANCE*

It is not only residential farming that contributes to agrarian landscapes in the world. On both sides of the ocean, low-intensity migratory livestock systems occur that contribute to local landscapes, mainly in mountainous regions. The seasonal migration of livestock often follows the cyclical changes of nature related to precipitation (from dry to wet, for example, in Africa) or temperature (from cold to warm, for example, in Europe and North America).

Short-distance migration, from summer to winter pastures and back, is quite common in mountainous areas. Less common, but still undertaken on a large scale, is long-distance migration, commonly referred to by the French word *transhumance*, but having many national and regional equivalents. Shepherds and their livestock (usually sheep and goats) may move over tens to hundreds of kilometres between lowland winter pastures and mountainous summer pastures. These migratory systems significantly contribute to traditional rural landscapes and cultures.

In this chapter we will describe examples of transhumance in Europe's Mediterranean and Balkans regions and an example from the United States, where a similar farming system has been imported on a smaller scale in the state of Idaho.

Die Weidewirtschaft umfasst immer noch Tausende von Hirten und Millionen von Viehbeständen. Es ist von entscheidender Bedeutung, dass die Lebensräume in den Bergen offen gehalten werden und somit Lebensraum für viele Pflanzen- und Tierarten geboten wird. Auch der Iberische Luchs (Seite 131) ist an die Weidewirtschaft gebunden, da er sich von kleinen Weidelandtieren wie Kaninchen und den Kadavern von Weidetieren ernährt.

Las trashumancia aún implica a miles de pastores y millones de cabezas de ganado. Se trata de una actividad fundamental para mantener despejados los hábitats de montaña y dejar así espacio para muchas especies animales y vegetales. El propio lince ibérico (página 131) está vinculado a la trashumancia, ya que se alimenta de pequeños animales que viven en los prados, como los conejos, y de reses muertas de rebaños trashumantes con enfermedades.

La transhumance occupe encore des milliers de bergers et implique des millions de tête de bétail. Il est crucial de maintenir les habitats montagnards ouverts et de permettre ainsi à de nombreuses espèces végétales et animales de s'y adapter. Le lynx ibérique lui-même (page 131) est lié à la transhumance, car il se nourrit de petits herbivores comme les lapins et de carcasses d'animaux morts durant la transhumance.

Transhumance still involves thousands of shepherds and millions of livestock. It is also crucial to keep mountain habitats open and thus provide room for many plant and animal species. Even the Iberian lynx (page 131) is linked to transhumance, as it feeds on small grassland animals like rabbits and off the carcasses of diseased transhumant flock.

Transhumance in Europe

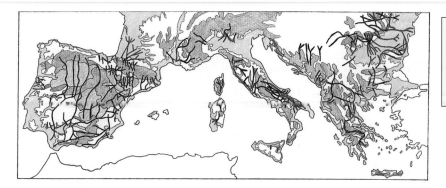

Main transhumance droves in southern Europe
- ■ high mountain chains above 1000 metres
- ■ inland plains above 200 metres
- ■ river plains and coastal land below 200 metres

Composed by W. Vos with data from Braudel (1966), with reference to Müller (1938) and Lemot (1999).

Although its roots are not exactly known, transhumance is indisputably a very old phenomenon. It may have been introduced in the Neolithic period soon after the invention of livestock farming with sheep (in Turkey) and goats (in Iran), in roughly 8,000 BC. There are early written records of transhumance, including a tale that two transhumant shepherds rescued Oedipus on the Greek Mount Kithairon in Sophocles' tragedy Oedipus Rex (430 BC). Written records indicate that transhumance occurred in Spain even before it was conquered by

the Romans. Today, transhumance is still practiced in the mountainous regions surrounding the Mediterranean Sea, including the Balkans, the eastern part of Turkey (Kurdistan), and the Middle East (Syria, Jordan etc.). Long-distance livestock movements also take place in other mountainous areas throughout Europe, from the northern parts of the Alps and the central European Carpathians to the British Isles and the Norwegian mountains.

Shepherds who practice transhumance usually have a fixed residence (usually in a lowland village or in the mountains) and travel mostly fixed routes with their livestock. There are at least three kinds of transhumance:

- Regular transhumance: moving the animals from lowland pastures to mountain pastures in early summer and back in the autumn, with stubble grazing on the way back and in the lowlands, sometimes on leased land, in exchange for fertilising the land (droppings).
- Inverse transhumance: herds descending the mountains in autumn to graze lowland pastures.
- Mixed transhumance: where shepherds live halfway between the lowlands and the mountains.

As the map indicates, there are many different transhumance centres and transhumance routes. The paths the livestock travel have special names in the regions involved — for example, *drayes*, *drailles* in the Languedoc, *carraïres* in the Provence, *camis ramaders* in the eastern Pyrenees, *cañadas* in Castilia (smaller droves *cordeles* or *veredas*), *tratturi* or *trazzere* in Italy, *vlachóstrata* in Greece and *drumul oilor* in Romania. Seasonal migration of livestock occurs with sheep, goats, cattle, horses and, in earlier times in Portugal, even with pigs. Most widespread is the transhumance with sheep and goats, which occurs in landscapes made of limestone and otherwise dry and poor soils. The shepherds milk their animals as they travel and sell the dairy products to people along the route. Wool, however, is primarily sold at markets.

At its prime, transhumance accounted for roughly 2.5 million animals in Greece (early 20th century), 1.5 million in the Provence (19th century), 5.5 million in southern Italy (17th century) and 3 million in Spain (14th century). Although the share of transhumance in Mediterranean livestock systems has been declining in some regions more than in others, it is still quite substantial, encompassing many millions of animals. In Greece, for example, 20 per cent of the national herd, or two million animals, are moved via transhumance.

In some areas a decline began in the second half of the 19th century. Pastures, fields, woodlands and long-distance paths became increasingly abandoned. The share of transhumance is now said to be rather stable in the Mediterranean and Alpine regions, thanks to additional income from subsidies and secondary incomes. More than a century ago, the modernisation of transport resulted in some transhumance occurring by train in Spain and Italy, and today, in some regions, transport by truck prevails.

Values and Benefits

- **Culture and history.** Transhumance is related to many cultural and historical traditions. Part of this tradition includes feasts in the villages when the flocks pass or return.
- **Habitat.** Transhumance is an essential part of grassland ecosystems in mountains, lowlands, and along droves. The grazing and browsing create open, mosaic-like patches, providing room for many plant and animal species. Predators (raptors, wolves, lynx) feed on the carcasses of transhumant animals that die in route and from wildlife that rely on the grazed areas (such as rabbits and partridges). In Spain, the endangered Iberian lynx is connected with transhumance.
- **Genetic diversity.** Transhumance is also of great importance to the genetic diversity of livestock, as it frequently relies on specific breeds. In Romania, for example, mainly local sheep breeds (Walachian or Zackel, Tsigai, Tsurcana and Ruda) are used for transhumance. The future of all these breeds strongly depends on the future of transhumance.

Challenges and Threats

- **Low profitability**. The life of the transhumant shepherds is difficult, and the job does not pay well. The revenues of transhumant systems are declining even faster than those of residential livestock systems.

- **Decreasing farmland**. Intensification of agriculture combined with a decrease of farmed land due to urban expansion and afforestation of pastures (as a result of attractive payments) reduce the room for transhumance.

- **Private lands**. Tensions with farmers whose lands are crossed may be very problematic, for instance on private land that was formerly state-owned in Central and Eastern European regions.

- **Route access**. The transport routes have become less accessible or even (temporarily) closed as a result of perceived veterinary risk, strict transport regulations following outbreaks of foot-and-mouth and other contagious diseases, more dense motorway infrastructure, canals, storage lakes and built-up area on transhumance routes, and lowland areas are increasingly used for intensive crops, tourist resorts, and other venues. War, political changes and the establishment of new states and boundaries, especially in the Balkans, have also complicated transhumance.

- **Lack of supports**. Sedentary farmers have better access to government subsidies.

Public Policies and Incentives

- **Financial incentives**. In regions within the European Union where transhumance is practiced, farmers can obtain area payments for less-favoured areas and headage premiums for sheep and goats. In areas with natural handicaps or for animals used in transhumance systems, there is a modest additional premium.

- **Policy gap**. At the same time, the CAP and its reforms pose a threat to migratory livestock systems. Not only because of veterinary legislation, but also because of the increasing focus on area or farm-based payments as a result of 'decoupling'. Since many transhumance farmers do not own or rent pastures on a long-term basis, EU support is not tailored to these kinds of livestock systems. Despite growing awareness on the significance of transhumance systems and frequent farmer and non-governmental organisation proposals to support livestock systems, the problem is not yet properly addressed in EU policies. In addition, the eligibility criteria for EU subsidies (education, professional skills, farm management plans) have become very strict.

- **Beyond the EU**. Non-EU countries, like Romania, have their own support systems for livestock farming. Being mainly semi-subsistent, the support only partly benefits transhumant systems.

Transhumance in Romania

In Eastern Europe and the Balkans, there are three important transhumance centres — the Carpathians, the Macedonian area (Macedonia, Northern Greece, Albania, Southern Bulgaria, Croatia) and the Dinarian Mountains (Bosnia-Herzegovina). In Romania, transhumance flourished widely in the 18th and 19th centuries, when the borders were still open. Around the turn of the 19th century, it was practiced by some 139 mountain villages, and involved 20 percent of the Romanian sheep. Data from 1931 for the Sibiu district indicate that the average sheep flock included 1,300 sheep, but flocks as large as 40,000 animals have also been recorded.

The decline in transhumance began after 1920, when the routes were cut off by the Romanian borders. Due to competition for land, the tensions between shepherds and residential livestock farmers increased. Between 1952 and 1955, transhumance was even forbidden. After 1955, government incentives boosted wool prices to three to four times the world market price, but the support was short-lived, ending abruptly with the dawn of the Romanian Revolution in 1989. Consequently, between 1989 and 2001 the number of sheep dropped dramatically — by about one-third — the sharpest reductions taking place among big farmers (who own sheep and hire shepherds). The 'private'

sheep-owning shepherds, who are much more self-supporting, were less affected. Still, there are some production subsidies for milk and meat, but only a minority of farmers apply.

In the Ciucaş Mountains, southeast of the city of Braşov, several shepherd camps exist. The camp manager takes care of the division of tasks (herding, cheese-making), provides the shepherds with food and drink, collects the cheese and distributes it to the villages. The sheep are milked two to three times a day, and after each milking the cheese production starts. The transhumance route is about 300 kilometres long, requiring about one month to complete. However, the journey usually takes longer, as the herds graze along the way. The shepherds own or rent the mountain pastures and rent the lowland pastures. Rental prices have not been raised since the revolution. Grazing underway is not paid for, however, which causes severe tensions with residential farmers. The problem warrants active policy incentives to reduce tensions and enhance sustainability.

Transhumance in the United States

Transhumance is not a word used in the United States. However, the seasonal movement of livestock between upland and lowland pastures is a long-standing agricultural practice with deep historical connections to the Scottish, Basque and Peruvian immigrants that have been coming to North America for more than 150 years. In fact, there is a resurgence of recognition of the historical and cultural importance of transhumance going on in the United States today, reflected in the Trailing of the Sheep Festival that is held in Ketchum and Hailey, Idaho every fall.

In mid-October, this beautiful mountain region is the setting for what the local residents call America's version of the 'Running of the Bulls'. As their immigrant ancestors have done for centuries, both in the US and in Europe, shepherds move their flocks to mountain pastures in the spring, north of the resort towns of Ketchum and Sun Valley, then south in the fall, through the Wood River Valley, to desert winter grazing areas. Normally, the flocks of between 1,500 and 1,800 animals move down side streets and along sheep easements lining State Highway 75 to complete their annual trek. But for one day each year, the city of Ketchum closes its Main Street to traffic, allowing the migration to move through town in celebration of the local history. Residents and visitors who line up for the big parade see the sheep led through town by Basque and Peruvian musicians and dancers and Scottish bagpipers — the groups that figure prominently in the history western sheepherding. It is a festive atmosphere as they watch and 'trail' behind the sheep, reliving the slower pace of a bygone era.

In the early 1900s, the Wood River Valley was second only to Sydney, Australia as an international sheep centre. The combination of high mountain meadows and fertile river valley pastures in close proximity was ideal. Today, however, the area has given way to tourism and vast residential growth. This, coupled with crippling economic losses among sheep ranchers, has forced many families out of business. Where at one time over several hundred thousand sheep moved through the area, fewer than 20,000 still make the trip.

Recognizing the need to link history and culture to survive as third-generation sheep producers, John and Diane Peavey created the idea of an annual festival as a way of bringing attention to the serious challenges facing ranchers. In 1990, the Peaveys invited area residents to join them in trailing one of their sheep bands down the valley. School children and adults alike participated, and the idea for the Trailing of the Sheep was born. Today this three-day event celebrates the music, dance, food, work skills and personal stories of shepherds and sheep ranchers. It has sparked the imagination of visitors from all around the United States who come to explore the Old West in the quiet of a fall weekend.

Perspectives & Policy Suggestions

In this book we see a rich variety of agrarian landscapes and the many challenges and threats they are facing. Ironically, some of these breathtaking landscapes are categorised as 'Less Favoured Areas'. While this may be true from a narrow agrarian perspective, from a wider perspective, these landscapes are among our most favoured. But as we have seen, most of these landscapes will lose much of their values, or will vanish, if all decisions are simply left to the main players in the market. Markets can perform a lot of useful functions, but they can rarely preserve or create public goods like scenic beauty, cultural heritage or biodiversity.

If we wish to preserve these landscapes and their values we need active public policies and political leadership. Conservation policy is a good start, but we also need to address trade, rural development and technology policies — on all levels, from local to global. Any number of policies, however, would be useless without the enthusiasm and creativity of the people in the region — from farmers and small town residents to the indigenous people of Scandinavia and North America. And in an ever further urbanising world, we must have active support from the people in our cities in order to address these policy issues. Furthermore, city dwellers play a critical role as consumers of products grown on the landscapes at stake.

Observations

Before we provide specific suggestions, here are some preliminary observations.

First, some people think that agriculture is just like other branches of the economy, for example manufacturing or mining. But what other part of the economy can provide beautiful scenery and social, cultural and biological diversity on such a scale?

Second, some economists claim that agriculture should simply be treated the same as other economic sectors. Under this logic, they argue farming should be subjected to world market forces, no matter how distorted these markets may be or how devastating such a policy would be to farmers and their surrounding communities. On this advice, we are highly skeptical. Every sector in the economy operates with regulation. The world agricultural market remains today a dumping market — where prices are manipulated to get rid of expensive surpluses. Even the most efficient farms cannot survive 'rigged' low market prices.

Third, there is a belief among some that agricultural prices should be forced down in order to benefit consumers. As we have seen in preceding chapters, this approach threatens a number of key values and benefits. When prices are low it is more and more difficult for farmers to operate their farms in a sustainable way — taking into account the protection of the environment, and scenic and cultural values. In addition, artificially low prices may harm consumers as they tend to stimulate food consumption, which can pose serious health risks. We know that too much sugar, salt and saturated fat, and not enough fruit and vegetables is a threat to our well-being. The World Health Organization recently rang the alarm bell on the 'epidemic' of obesity, diabetes, cancer and heart diseases. We need to get away from overproduction and overconsumption. This requires higher rather than lower prices for most of our farm products.

Of course it would be naive to think that higher farmgate and food prices per se can save many landscapes. We also need policy measures to locally stimulate extensification and encourage management of land for the full range of values it can provide.

Removing Policy Obstacles

As we have seen, there are some good elements in the current US and EU agricultural policies. At the same time, we have identified a number of serious policy obstacles to the preservation of the many benefits of agrarian landscapes, not only in the US Farm Bill and the EU Common Agricultural Policy (CAP), but also in bi-lateral and multilateral trade agreements.

For example, under pressure from the World Trade Organisation (WTO), the EU has recently taken major steps in decoupling payments from production. In some regions this is detrimental to landscape management. It stimulates livestock farmers to end grazing in those regions where grazing may not be profitable in and of itself, but is necessary to maintain the associated values of the landscape. In situations like these, the WTO should allow more coupling of payments to production.

The CAP also has a 'second pillar' providing payments for agri-environment measures and for 'Less Favoured Areas'. The levels of these payments are often low, since agricultural income is still used as a reference, and only costs incurred and income foregone may be compensated. That compensation, in some cases, is not enough to attract a sufficient number of farmers and thus to preserve the landscape. Higher payments should be allowed where necessary. These payments should be decoupled from agriculture and recoupled to green services, i.e. landscape management. Trading partners do not have to worry here, since these payments will reduce rather than enhance production.

Similarly, under WTO pressure, the US government has been eliminating or reducing key price support and natural resource conservation programmes.

Both the Farm Bill and the CAP contain agri-environment schemes. In the US, these policies are only now being implemented. In the EU, where there has been a longer history of agri-environment schemes, these policies are shown to be effective in some cases, but not yet in others. For example, they are not adequate for mountain farming and for complex production systems like transhumance and the montados in Portugal. In some regions they even enhance simplification and intensification. Clearly, more tailor-made schemes are needed.

Policy Mix

The following policy mix may provide basic conditions for sustainable development of agriculture combined with tailor-made schemes designed to maintain many of its natural, scenic and cultural values.

1. General policies to keep agriculture economically viable.

Every policy to support sustainable development and non-market values of agriculture should start with a general policy aimed at providing an economic basis for sustainable agriculture in the marketplace.

The first and least costly way is to create a sound economic basis for farming by safeguarding 'fair' prices — prices that reflect costs on efficient small and moderate-sized farms. To maintain balance in supply and demand, it is important that price support policies include both the phasing out of price dumping on the world market and mechanisms to manage supply to meet demand. Classic options include marketing orders, set-aside and quotas. New options include higher taxes on production-stimulating, environmentally-damaging inputs, like nitrogen. This approach could simultaneously reduce production and emissions. In times of food shortage and high food prices, these restrictions can then be relaxed to raise production again.

A second approach is to compensate farmers for price cuts in such a way that production is not enhanced — so-called decoupled support. This is the system the EU has chosen. While such support is more acceptable for trading partners than classic price supports, it has its disadvantages.

First, since this support paves the way for price cuts, it may indirectly enhance overconsumption and thereby contribute to obesity among consumers. Second, decoupled support can still stimulate production, albeit less than price supports. This approach also allows the food industry to export to the world market at prices below cost, which is a kind of dumping. Since only rich countries can afford paying such support, it may selectively harm developing countries where farmers may be driven out of business, and citizens may become subject to the hazards of an increasingly unreliable world market.

Clearly there are problems in every policy option. In order to respect this complexity, which results from multiple, interacting dynamics, we should avoid any form of 'one-size-fits-all' solutions. For instance, there is hardly any policy that fits both developed and developing countries.

2. General policies supporting sustainable agriculture.

Although fair prices are the fundamental basis for keeping farmers on the land, they cannot alone help to move the entire sector towards greater sustainability. This requires much more conscious and targeted measures.

A key element is internalizing more of the costs, including the environmental costs. The nitrogen tax mentioned above may be an example of how this could be accomplished. This would help to reduce three emissions: nitrate, ammonia and the greenhouse gas dinitrousoxide. Of course, this type of measure will also raise production costs in those countries where such a step is taken. This may create unfair competition from other countries who fail to internalize environmental costs. Border measures will then be needed to ensure that environmentally or socially subsidized imports are not allowed to destroy the farmers who are moving towards greater sustainability.

Other options include direct assistance to farmers in the process of adopting sustainable development measures and cross compliance, linking agricultural support to environmental and animal welfare standards. This has recently been introduced in the EU, and experience is being obtained.

3. Specific programs for specific landscapes and activities.

For the maintenance of specific landscapes and activities in specific regions, even more targeted policies are required. Options include:

- Agri-environment payments like those in the US Farm Bill's Conservation Reserve Program and in the agri-environment programmes of the EU's CAP.
- Financial compensation for farmers of valuable landscapes who face physical handicaps, like steep slopes. The EU already has a Least Favoured Area scheme, which, however, needs to be more tailored for complex agro-ecosystems like mountain farming, transhumance and montados.
- Supporting local private initiatives, such as labelling schemes.
- Stimulating cooperation between farmers and citizens.

In this book we have looked at many good examples of such policies, both in the EU and North America.

4. Green space and spatial policies protecting valuable landscapes from urban sprawl and other threats.

Where agriculture is under pressure from urban sprawl or similar threats, public policies are vital. Such policies are primarily made at the local level, but for some very valuable landscapes, intervention by national and state or provincial governments may be justified. Remarkably, while the EU has a Birds Directive and a Habitat Directive, it lacks a Landscape Directive. The Council of Europe, which includes all European states, has recently endorsed a promising Landscape Convention. It includes a variety of policy instruments but lacks a budget. Here the EU should take its responsibility.

5. Promoting private initiatives

While government action is crucial, initiatives from farmers, other entrepreneurs and inhabitants of the region are central to a sustainable approach, especially if they attract capital from cities. Options include:

- Developing regional labels and promoting them in the market.
- Developing markets for 'green services', eco- and agri-tourism and landscape sponsoring.
- Experiments with shared farmer/citizen landownership and management.

Some such initiatives have good opportunities near cities, while others (like wildlife tourism) are more likely to succeed further away from cities.

6. Innovation

It would be a major mistake to assume that preservation of valuable landscapes means no changes. These landscapes and the people who live and work on the land need continuous innovation, including improved equipment for land management, new arrangements between farmers and citizens and new methods of pest control. Here, government can provide financial support in research and testing, along with public education. In general, we need to move away from technologies and social relationships aimed at narrowly-focused efficiency and move towards multi-purpose technologies and relationships serving broader society and the planet.

WHO WILL PAY THE BILL?

It seems obvious that no single party can pay the entire bill for the preservation and management of valuable landscapes. Fortunately, financing may come from various sources:

- The food consumer paying fair prices for food in general.
- Local and other concerned consumers buying regional produce, increasing the market share of local production.
- Taxpayers paying for the management of particular landscapes, for investment, innovation and local public–private initiatives.
- Tourists paying for facilities provided by farmers.
- Property-owners who see their houses and lands gaining value from scenic beauty.
- Water industries paying for good farming practices and innovation.
- Companies paying for maintaining scenic beauty in their vicinity or sponsoring specific landscapes.

This book has shown examples of these kinds of innovative financing mechanisms.

CREATING THE POLITICAL WILL: THE MULTI-STAKEHOLDER APPROACHES

Given the multiple values and benefits of many agricultural landscapes, it is clear that we cannot leave landscape and farming policies solely to governments and to the dominant players in the agricultural market. We need multi-stakeholder participation at all levels: local, state, federal and EU, across the Atlantic and between north and south. Experience has shown that such participation can be highly productive when participants respect one another and share a common purpose.

The successful examples in North American and the EU highlighted in this book demonstrate that this is more than theory. We have real choices.

ACKNOWLEDGEMENTS

First of all, we wish to thank the Dutch Ministry of Agriculture, Nature and Food Quality for its major financial support for this project.

An equally important contribution was made by the many people who helped us writing the book: by providing information and/or pictures, by facilitating interviews or by commenting on draft texts:

LOWLANDS, WETLANDS & FLOODPLAINS
Piotr Marczakiewicz and Adam Sieńko, Biebrza National Park
Tomasz Pezold, IUCN Programme Office for Central Europe, Warsaw
Cal Thorson, USDA-ARS Northern Great Plains Research Laboratory, US
Dan Imhoff, Watershed Media, US
Fred Kirschenmann, Leopold Center for Sustainable Development, Iowa State University, US

UPLANDS & MOUNTAINS
Clunie Keenleyside, Crex Consultants, United Kingdom
Gwyn Jones, European Forum on Nature Conservation and Pastoralism
Chris Chesterton, Rural Development Service Yorkshire and the Humber, Department for Environment, Food and Rural Affairs (DEFRA)
Hervé Cortot, Parc National Des Écrins, France
Pierre-Yves Motte, farmers' president in Les Écrins, France
Davorin Koren and Jurij Dobravec, Triglav National Park, Slovenia
Guido Plassmann, Alparc – Réseau Alpin des Espaces Protégés
Peter Veen, VeenEcology BV, The Netherlands
Karen Rauter, Watershed Agricultural Council, New York, US

BOREAL LANDSCAPES
Thordis Samuelsson, Jönköping County Administrative Board
Gun Rudquist, Swedish Society for Nature Conservation
Sven-Inge Ågren, farmer at Eksjö, Småland
Agneta Börjesson and Birgitta Fluur, Swedish Board of Agriculture
Jan-Ivar Rönnbäck, Norrbotten County Administrative Board
Brian Churchill, Peace Habitat and Conservation Endowment Trust, British Columbia, Canada
Herb Barbolet, Farm Folk, City Folk, Vancouver, British Columbia, Canada

SEMI-ARID LANDSCAPES
Teresa Pinto-Correia, Universidade de Évora, Portugal
Willem Vos, Wageningen University and Research Centre, The Netherlands
Juan J. Oñate, Universidad Autónoma de Madrid, Spain
Juan de Mesa, farmer, Spain
Dan Imhoff, Watershed Media, US
Sue and Tony Norris, Arizona, US

MEDITERRANEAN LANDSCAPES
Patrizia Rossi and Filomena Petruzzi, Lega Italiana Protezione Uccelli (LIPU), BirdLife Italy
Roberto Soragnese, farmer in Bovino, Italy
Elisabeth Ptak, Marin Agricultural Land Trust, California, US
Lisa Hamilton, California, US
Michael Straus, Straus Communications, California, US

ISLAND LANDSCAPES
Paraskevi Dilana – Greek Ministry of Rural Development and Food
Stela Kasiola – SantoWines, Santorini
Tilavgis Dimitriou, Samos
Evert Zorgdrager, island farmer
Sabien van Heusden, Waddenvereniging, The Netherlands
Carl I. Evensen, University of Hawaii at Manoa, Hawaii, US
Franco Salmoiraghi, Hawaii, US

LARGE-SCALE CEREAL LANDSCAPES
Linda Gallet, Dominique Thepin, Institut d'Amenagement et d'Urbanisme de la Region d'Île-de-France (IAURIF).
Patricia Larbouret, Direction régionale et interdépartementale de l'agriculture et de la forêt d'Île-de-France (DRIAF)
Mr. Delataille, Chambre Interdepartementale d'Agriculture d'Île-de-France
Tim King, Minnesota, US
Mark Muller, Institute for Agriculture and Trade Policy, Minnesota, US
Jim Kleinschmit, Institute for Agriculture and Trade Policy, US
Linda Meschke, Blue Earth River Basin Initiative, Minnesota, US
Paula Westmoreland, Minnesota, US
Tony Thompson, farmer, Minnesota, US

MIGRATORY LIVESTOCK PRODUCTION: *TRANSHUMANCE*
Condrea Drăgănescu, Institute of Biology and Animal Nutrition, Bukarest, Romania
Willem Vos, Wageningen University and Research Centre, The Netherlands
Sally Huband, former Pastoral Project Officer Scottish Agricultural College
Rob Jongman and Marta Perez Soba, Alterra, The Netherlands
Diane Peavey, Idaho, US

Also thanks to Adriaan Guldemond and Harriët de Ruiter (Centre for Agriculture and environment) for their ecological advice during several stages of the book. Enid Blekman of Snelvertaler for translating photo captions into Spanish, French and German. In North America, thanks to Andi McDaniel, Michelle Wilwerding and Monica Siems for their editorial work; to Kathy Hiltsley for her administrative assistance and to Becky Fromberg for her proofreading assistance.

PHOTOGRAPHERS

TITLE PAGE, TABLE OF CONTENTS, PREFACE, INTRODUCTION

p.2 Josep Ferrer / Alamy Images, p.5 Franco Salmoiraghi, p.6 top left: Renata and Marek Kosinscy, top right: Joe Cornish, Arcaid / Alamy Images, bottom left: Vincent Van Gogh, Kröller-Müller Museum, The Netherlands, bottom right: Franco Salmoiraghi, p.7 top left: Donald A. Pettit, top right: Dan Imhoff, bottom left: Yann Arthus-Bertrand / Altitude, France, bottom right: Steve Platzer, p.8 Ove Källström / Norrlandia, Sweden, p.10 Corbis, p.12 Rui Cunha (www.rcl-imagem.pt), Portugal, p.14 Karrilyn Vince, courtesy of Peace Habitat and Conservation Endowment Trust

LOWLANDS, WETLANDS & FLOODPLAINES

p.16 Renata and Marek Kosinscy, p.18 Paul Paris fotografie, The Netherlands, p.19 left: Aad van Paassen, The Netherlands, right: Derek Stone / Alamy Images, p.20 Paul Terwan, The Netherlands, p.21 Paul Terwan, The Netherlands, p.22 Creatas / Dynamic Graphics Group / Alamy Images, p.24 Chuck Haney, p.25 Chuck Haney, p.27 Dan Imhoff, p.28 left: Klosowski Brothers, Poland, right: Klosowski Brothers, Poland, p.29 Paul Terwan, The Netherlands, p.30 Tomasz Pezold, IUCN, Poland, p.31 Biebrza National Park

UPLANDS & MOUNTAINS

p.32 Joe Cornish, Arcaid / Alamy Images, p.33 Karen Rauter, courtesy of Watershed Agricultural Council, p.35 Jorge Tutor / MTP Network, p.36 left: Laurie Campbell / RSPB-Images, right: Ernie Janes / RSPB-Images, p.38 Mediacolor`s / Alamy Images, p.39 left: Bertrand Bodin / Photothèque du Parc National des Écrins, right: Werner Dieterich / Alamy Images, p.41 Bertrand Bodin / Photothèque du Parc National des Écrins, p.44 Karen Rauter, courtesy of Watershed Agricultural Council, p.45 Andy Olenick, p.46 Vickers and Beechler, courtesy of Watershed Agricultural Council, p.47 Vickers and Beechler, courtesy of Watershed Agricultural Council, p.48 Vickers and Beechler, courtesy of Watershed Agricultural Council, p.49 Karen Rauter, courtesy of Watershed Agricultural Council

BOREAL LANDSCAPES

p.50 Donald A. Pettit, p.51 Peter Gerdehag / Gerdehag Photography AB, Sweden, p.53 Peter Gerdehag / Gerdehag Photography AB, Sweden, p.54 bottom left: Steve Knell / RSPB-Images, upper left: John Crellin / www.floralimages.co.uk, right: Sven-Inge Ågren, Sweden, p.56 Donald A. Pettit, p.58 Donald A. Pettit, p.59 Donald A. Pettit, p.61 Kate Kärrberg / Naturbild, Sweden, p.62 top: Tomas Utsi Naturfoto AB, Sweden, p.63 Kate Kärrberg / Naturbild, Sweden, p.65 Clark Mishler

SEMI-ARID LANDSCAPES

p.66 Tony Marinella, p.69 Rui Cunha (www.rcl-imagem.pt), Portugal, p.70 top: Pascal Dubois (http://cote-nature.net), bottom: Pascal Dubois (http://cote-nature.net), p.71 Rui Cunha (www.rcl-imagem.pt), Portugal, p.72 Willem Vos, The Netherlands, p.73 Willem Vos, The Netherlands, p.74 Juan J. Oñate, Spain, p.76 Carlos Palacín, p.78 Juan J. Oñate, Spain, p.79 Elado García, p.81 Peter Friederici, p.82 Dan Imhoff, p.83 Roberto Carra, p. 84 Roberto Carra, p. 85 Roberto Carra

MEDITERRANEAN LANDSCAPES

p.86 Aliki Sapountzi / Aliki Image Library / Alamy Images, p.88 Ken Welsh / Alamy Images, p.89 Vincent Van Gogh, Kröller-Müller Museum, The Netherlands, p.90 left: P. Jaccod / LIPU (BirdLife Italy), p.92 F. Petruzzi / LIPU (BirdLife Italy), p.93 Thislife Pictures / Alamy Images, p.94 Frank S. Balthis, p.96 Frank S. Balthis, p.97 Frank S. Balthis,

ISLAND LANDSCAPES

p.98 Tom Pfeiffer / www.decadevolcano.net, p.100 Paraskevi Dilana, p.101 Paul Terwan, The Netherlands, p.102 Carlos Sanchez / RSPB-Images, p.105 Jerry DeWitt, p.106 Aerophoto Eelde, The Netherlands, p.108 Marleen Swart, The Netherlands, p.109 James de Bounevialle / Alamy Images, p.111 Bill Brooks / Alamy Images, p.112 Franco Salmoiraghi, p.113 Carl I. Evensen, p.114 Franco Salmoiraghi, p.115 Franco Salmoiraghi

LARGE-SCALE CEREAL LANDSCAPES

p.116 Yann Arthus-Bertrand / Altitude, France, p.119 Kader Meguedad / Alamy Images, p.120 left: Roger Tidman / RSPB-Images, right: Paul Terwan, The Netherlands, p.122 Rick McFerrin, p.126 Corbis, p.127 Ricardo Salvador, Iowa State University,

MIGRATORY LIVESTOCK PRODUCTION: *TRANSHUMANCE*

p.128 Bertrand Bodin / Photothèque du Parc National des Écrins, p.130 Robert Harding Picture Library Ltd / Alamy Images, p.131 Jose B. Ruiz / Nature Picture Library, p.133 Annette Mertens, Italy, p.135 Steve Platzer

SPECIES LIST

Mammals

English Name	Scientific Name
Alpine Ibex	*Capra ibex*
Arctic Grayling	*Thymallus arcticus*
Badger	*Meles meles*
Beaver (American)	*Castor canadensis*
Bison	*Bison bison*
Black Bear	*Ursus americanus*
Brown Hare	*Lepus europeaus*
Caribou (US form for reindeer)	*Rangifer tarandus*
Chamois	*Rupicapra rupicapra*
Elk (British: Wapiti)	*Cervus canadensis*
Fisher	*Martes pennanti*
Flying Squirrels	*Glaucomys*
Genet	*Genetta genetta*
Grizzly Bear	*Ursus arctos*
Iberian Lynx	*Lynx pardinus*
Jackal	*Canis aureus*
Jaguar	*Felis onca*
Marten (American)	*Martes americana*
Moose (British: Elk)	*Alces alces*
Mountain Lion (Puma)	*Felis concolor*
Pardel Lynx (=Iberian lynx)	*Lynx pardinus*
Pygmy Shrew	*Sorex hoyi*
Reindeer	*Rangifer tarandus*
Roedeer	*Capreolus capreolus*
Walleye	*Sander vitreus*
Wild Cat	*Felix silvestris*
Wolf	*Canis lupus*

Birds

English Name	Scientific Name
American Kestrel	*Falco sparverius*
Aquatic Warbler	*Acrocephalus paludicola*
Azure-winged Magpie	*Cyanopica cyana*
Bald Eagle	*Haliaeetus leucocephalus*
Bearded Vulture	*Gypaetus barbatus*
Black-capped Chickadee	*Parus atricapillus*
Black Kite	*Milvus migrans*
Black Stork	*Ciconia nigra*
Black Vulture	*Aegypius monachus*
Black-bellied Sandgrouse	*Pterocles orientalis*
Black-shouldered Kite	*Elanus caeruleus*
Black-tailed Godwit	*Limosa limosa*
Bleu-winged Teal	*Anas discors*
Bonelli's Eagle	*Hieraaetus fasciatus*
Brent Geese	*Branta bernicla*
Burrowing Owl	*Athene cunicularia*
Calandra Lark	*Melanocorypha calandra*
Canvasback Duck	*Aythya valisineria*
Corncrake	*Crex crex*
Crane	*Grus grus*
Crested Lark	*Galerida cristata*
Crossbill	*Loxia sp.*
Curlew	*Numenius arquata*
Eagle Owl	*Bubo bubo*
European Crane	*Grus grus*
Gadwall	*Anas strepera*
Golden Plover	*Pluvialis apricaria*
Great Bustard	*Otis tarda*
Great Snipe	*Gallinago media*
Grey Partridge	*Perdix perdix*
Griffon Vulture	*Gyps fulvus*
Hen Harrier	*Circus cyaneus*
Hoopoe	*Upupa epops*
Imperial Eagle	*Aquila heliaca*
Kinglet	*Reguluscuvier*
Lapwing	*Vanellus vanellus*
Lesser Kestrel	*Falco naumanni*
Little Bustard	*Tetrax tetrax*
Little Owl	*Athene noctua*
Merlin	*Falco columbarius*
Montagu's Harrier	*Circus pygargus*
Partridge	*Perdix perdix*
Peregrine Falcon	*Falco peregrinus*
Pin-tailed Sandgrouse	*Pterocles alchata*
Quail	*Coturnix coturnix*
Raven	*Corvus corax*
Red Grouse	*Lagopus lagopus scoticus*
Red-necked Nightjar	*Caprimulgus ruficollis*
Redshank	*Tringa totanus*
Ruff	*Philomachus pugnax*
Rufous Hummingbird	*Selasphorus rufus*
Scops Owl	*Otus scops*
Short-toed Lark	*Calandrella brachydactyla*
Stone Curlew	*Burhinus oedicnemus*
Tawny Pipit	*Anthus campestris*

Twite	*Carduelis flavirostris*
Whinchat	*Saxicola ruberta*
White Stork	*Ciconia ciconia*
White Wagtail	*Motacilla alba*
Whooping Crane	*Grus americana*
Woodlark	*Lullula arborea*
Yellowhammer	*Emberiza citrinella*

Fish

Lake Char	*Salvelinus namaycush*
Northern Pike	*Esox lucius*
Walleye	*Stizostedion vitreum*
Arctic Grayling	*Thymallus arcticus*
Rainbow Trout	*Oncorhynchus mykiss*

Plants

Alpine Pasqueflower	*Pulsatilla alpina*
American Beech	*Fagus grandifolia*
Aspen	*Populus sp.*
Balsam Fir	*Abies balsama*
Black Spruce	*Picea mariana*
Bluebell	*Campanula rotundifolia*
Blueberry	*Vaccinium sp.*
Bugleweed	*Ajuga reptans*
Calypso Orchid	*Calypso salisb.*
Cherry	*Prunus sp.*
Chestnut Oak	*Quercus prinus*
Cistus Ladanifer	*Cistus ladanifera*
Clusius Gentian	*Gentiana clusii*
Common Milkwort	*Polygala vulgaris*
Cork Oak	*Quercus Suber*
Corn Flower	*Centaurea cyanus*
Daffodil	*Narcissus sp.*
Devil's Bit Scabious	*Succisa pratensis*
Eastern White Pine	*Pinus strobus*
Evergreen Oak	*Quercus ilex*
Froelich's Gentian	*Gentiana froelichii*
Globeflower	*Trollius europeus*
Grace Ward	*Lithodora diffusa*
Great White Pine	*Pinus strobus*
Hemlock	*Tsuga sp.*
Holm Oak	*Quercus rotundifolia*
Julian Lousewort	*Pedicularis julica*
Juniper	*Juniperus sp.*
Lady's Bedstraw	*Galium verum*
Lady's Slippers	*Cypripedium acaule*
Lavender	*Lavendula sp.*

Lesser Burnet	*Pimpinella saxifraga*
Maple	*Acer sp.*
Marsh Marigold	*Caltha palustris*
Meadow Vetchling	*Lathyrus pratensis*
Olive	*Olea europae*
Pitch Pine	*Pinus rigida*
Ponderosa Pine	*Pinus ponderosa*
Red Oak	*Quercus rubra*
Red Poppy	*Papaver rhoea*
Red Spruce	*Picea rubens*
Rosemary	*Rosmarinus officinalis*
Shepherds Needle	*Scandix pecten veneris*
Spike Lavender	*Lavendula latifolia*
Tamarack	*Larix laricina*
Thyme	*Thymus spp*
Triglav Gentian	*Gentiana terglouensis*
Tulip	*Tulipa sp*
Verticillate Lousewort	*Pedicularis verticilata*
White Ash	*Fraxinus americana*
White Spruce	*Picea glauca*
Wood Cranesbill	*Geranium sylvaticum*
Yellow Birch	*Betula alleghaniensis*

Plants without English names

Cistus Ladanifera (Rockrose)
Genista sp. (Broom)
Genista triacanthos (Greenweed)
Lavandula latifolia (Spike Lavender)
Narcissus asturiensis (Daffodil)
Narcissus bulbocodicum nivalis (Daffodil)
Narcissus rupicola (Daffodil)
Retama sphaerocarpa (Retama)
Salvia lavandulifolia (Spanish Sage)
Tuberaria lignosa

FURTHER READING

GENERAL

Beaufoy, G., Baldock, D. & Clark, J. 1994. The Nature of Farming: Low Intensity Farming Systems in Nine European Countries. Institute for European Environmental Policy, London.

Baldock, D., G. Beaufoy, F. Brouwer & F. Godeschalk, 1997. Farming at the Margins: Abandonment or Redeployment of Agricultural Land in Europe. IEEP London / Agricultural Economics Research Institute, The Hague

Papers on the Pastoral Project at www1.sac.ac.uk/envsci/External/Pastoral

Website of the European Forum on Nature Conservation and Pastoralism www.efncp.org

Papers of the Frontis workshop on the future of the European cultural landscape 9-12 June 2002 The new dimensions of the European landscape at library.wur.nl/frontis/landscape/

LOWLANDS, WETLANDS & FLOODPLAINS

Borgers, G., A. Haartsen & P. Vesters 1997. Het Groene Hart – Een Hollands cultuurlandschap. Matrijs.

Kers, M. & H. Vuijsje 2001. Het Groene Hart. Inmerc, Wormer.

Winckler, S. 2004. Prairie: A North American Guide, Univeristy of Iowa Press, Iowa City, Iowa.

Savage, Page, and Williams, 2004. Prairie: A Natural History, Greystone Books, Vancouver, British Columbia.

Website Biebrza National Park: www.biebrza.org.pl

UPLANDS & MOUNTAINS

Website of the Pennine Dales ESA: www.defra.gov.uk/erdp/schemes/esas/stage1/pennine.htm

WWF – The Alps: a unique natural heritage – A Common Vision for the Conservation of their Biodiversity.

Mountain Areas in Europe: Analysis of mountain areas in EU member states, acceding and other European countries (2004). Nordregio – Nordic Centre for Spatial Development.

Website of the Watershed Agricultural Council: www.nycwatershed.org

Catskill Center for Conservation and Development website: www.catskillcenter.org

Alparc website: www.alparc.org

Euromontana website: www.euromontane.org

Website Triglav National Park: www.sigov.si/tnp

Website Les Écrins National Park: www.les-ecrins-parc-national.fr

BOREAL LANDSCAPES

The Environmental and Rural Development Plan for Sweden 2000-2006

Peace River Regional District Website: http://www.pris.bc.ca/prrd/

General information on North American boreal forest: http://www.borealforest.org/index.php

Website Swedish Board of Agriculture: www.sjv.se

Pettit, Donald A. 2001. The Peace: An Exploration in Photographs, PhotoGraphics, British Columbia, Canada.

Peace Habitat and Conservation Endowment Trust website: www.phacet.ca

SEMI-ARID LANDSCAPES

Suárez, F. Naveso, M.A. and De Juana, E. 1997. Farming in the drylands of Spain: birds of the pseudo steppes. In: Pain, D.J. and Pienkowski, M.W. Farming and Birds in Europe. Academic Press, London, pp. 297-330.

Pinto-Correia, T. & W. Vos, Multifunctionality in Mediterranean landscapes - Past and future. In: New dimensions of the European landscape, proceedings of Frontis workshop on the future of the European cultural landscape 9-12 June 2002, Wageningen.

Imhoff, Dan and Roberto Carra, 2003. Farming With the Wild: Enhancing Biodiversity on Farms and Ranches, University of California/Sierra Club Press, Berkeley, California.

Friederici, Peter and Rose Houk, 2004. A New Plateau: Sustaining the Lands and Peoples of Canyon Country, Renewing the Countryside, Minneapolis, USA.

MEDITERRANEAN LANDSCAPES

Beaufoy, G. 2001. EU policies for olive oil – unsustainable on all counts. WWF and BirdLife.

The Environmental Impact of Olive Oil Production in the European Union. European Forum on Nature Conservation and Pastoralism.

John Hart, Farming on the Edge, Marin Agricultural Land Trust, Pt. Reyes Station, California, University of California Press, 1991, Berkeley, California

Univ. of California Cooperative Extension, 2004. "Amazing but True... Facts about Agriculture in Marin County," ucce.ucdavis.edu/files/filelibrary/1410/5235.pdf.

Marin Agricultural Land Trust website: www.malt.org

ISLAND LANDSCAPES

Maria Mandraka: Towards sustainable islands: Naxos case study.

Off the coast of Europe – European construction and the problem of the islands. Study undertaken by Eurisles on the initiative of the Islands Commission of CPMR.

Carol Wilcox, Sugar Water: Hawaii's Plantation Ditches, University of Hawaii Press, 1998, Honolulu, Hawaii

Ira Rohter, A Green Hawaii: Sourcebook for Development Alternatives, Nā Kāne O Ka Malo Press,1992, Honolulu, Hawaii

Eurisles website: www.eurisles.org

SantoWines website: www.santowines.gr

LARGE-SCALE CEREAL LANDSCAPES

Monographie 1998 Chambre Interdepartementale d'Agriculture d'Île-de-France.

Blue Earth River Basin Intiative website : http://www.berbi.org/organization.htm

IAURIF website : www.iaurif.org

DRIAF website : www.ile-de-france.chambagri.fr

Minnesota River Valley National Wildlife Refuge webpage: http://www.nps.gov/miss/maps/model/mnrefuge.html

Joannides, J., et. al. 2001. Renewing the Countryside — Minnesota, Institute for Agriculture and Trade Policy, Minneapolis, Minnesota, USA

Orngard, S. et. al. 2003. Renewing the Countryside — Iowa, Renewing the Countryside, Minneapolis, Minnesota, USA

MIGRATORY LIVESTOCK PRODUCTION: *TRANSHUMANCE*

Braudel, F. 1966. La Méditerranée: La part du milieu. 3 Volumes. Librairie Armand Colin, Paris.

Lemot, T. 1999. Map: La grande transhumance ovine. Une pratique méditerranéenne. In: Transhumances. L'Alpe Nr. 3(1999). Glénat, Musée Dauphinois, Grenoble.

Müller, E. 1938. Die Herdenwanderungen im Mittelmeergebiet. In: Petermanns Geographische Mitteilungen.

Draganescu, C. 1998. Transhumance in Romania: Past, Present and Future. In: Archiva Zootechnica, Volume V.

The "Transhumont" project website : www.alterra-research.nl/transhumont

For North American background see http://www.trailingofthesheep.org/